A Journey Into Herbal Healing:
BlueFeather's Herbal

D1289627

This book is dedicated to the Spirit of the ancient Californian people who lived in paradise as sons and daughters of the Creator. To their living descendants, Chief Little Bear (Rudy Ortega) and his son, Standing Bear (Rudy Ortega Jr) who continue to inspire and lead many back to the sacred circle. And to the friends and caretakers of Satwewa who maintain the dreams and traditions of our ancestors.

A Journey Into Herbal Healing: BlueFeather's Herbal

RANDALL WHITE

DORSET PRESS
NEW YORK

Copyright © Randall White 1999

This edition published by Dorset Press by arrangement with Thomas C.
Lothian Pty Ltd
All rights reserved. No part of this publication may be reproduced,
stored in a retrieval system or transmitted in any form by any means
without the prior permission of the copyright owner. Enquiries should
be made to the publisher.

Disclaimer
This is not a manual for self-prescribing and readers are advised to seek
treatment from a qualified herbalist, naturopath or general practitioner as
required. Any person may develop an allergic reaction at any time to a
plant-derived substance, whether taken internally, as a food or for self-
medication, or used topically. Some plants are toxic if taken in large quantities or over long periods of time. Herbal remedies are not innocuous and
the effects of concomitant medication are potentally dangerous.
Professional advice should be sought for any persistant conditon. The
author and publisher cannot be held responsible for any injury or misad-
venture which may result from the use of information in this book.

Text design by Kim Roberts Design & Illustration
Illustrations by Julia McLeish

2001 Dorset Press
ISBN 0-7607-2188-2 *paperback*

Printed and Bound in the United States of America

01 02 03 04 MP 9 8 7 6 5 4 3 2 1

RRD-H

Contents

PART 4: the grandfathers

PART 5: the future of herbal healing

Acknowledgements

There are so many people who have helped me along this road of literary expression that it would take another book to acknowledge them all. It is a bit like recognizing one ant in a whole colony for his or her contribution to building the nest. Many have strengthened my ability to apply myself to the writing of this book but few are mentioned, not out of lack of recognition, but rather out of limited space.

Thanks firstly to the Creator, for the love and grace which gives us all the gifts needed to become a Human Being.

To my parents, who allowed me to be who and what I am. This type of freedom is a rare commodity in the world today. I thank my mother, Alice, for always being there for me, and for the support she has given throughout my life. I thank also my father, George, who for the last three years has been by my side counselling and offering me his unconditional love from the world of the Spirit, and for making his presence obvious enough for me to see clearly, even though I can be quite thick at times.

A special thanks to my sister, Marcia, and her husband Bill, for their generosity, and for supplying me with my first computer and enough knowledge and instruction to fulfill my dream of writing this book.

To my sister, Gerry, who played a far greater role in my personal development and growth than she will ever know.

To Barbara, who taught me more than any other Human Being how to live my life, and give up so much so that I could find out the truth about myself. It was not always pleasant, but it was always educational. How good it is to see her shining in her own light.

To my children, Leah and Nathan, who taught me the boundlessness of love. They are both the light of my life and have brought me the greatest of joys. May I always remember that they are gifts from God.

To my niece, Lizanne, who had the courage to show me that part of myself which I had left behind in Vietnam, and gave me the insight needed so that I could retrieve it.

Thanks to Jane Edmanson, and many others, for believing in my ability to change a stocklist into a book, and to Sally Moss for her patience, and Julia McLeish for her beautiful illustrations. They have all made the journey enjoyable.

To Tony and Lucy Hosemans, who treated me like family and supported me in all my endeavors.

And last but not least are those who have made their mark on my life, and each in their own way have made the road smooth or bumpy, but always uplifting. In no particular order, a big thank you to Ralph, Yvonne, Kerry, Oku, Brenda, Craig Carpenter, Lesley, Sonia, Steve, Bob, Marilyn, Manena, Natalie, Nitekowa, Coyote-man, Murrundindi, Tony Ghosthawk, Mary, Fiona, Vince, Terry, Dinea, and Kim.

Preface

If you have the patience and an appropriate attitude towards peoples often considered primitive or backward by our contemporary culture, there are places in the world where you will see herbal medicine practiced as it has been for thousands of generations, using techniques that bind us all to a common origin dating back over 100,000 years.

There was a time not so long ago when all cultures practiced these methods. But sadly, one by one, the light has been extinguished from such methods by hate, jealousy, greed and (most sadly of all) religion. During the last thousand years, millions of men and women have been tortured or killed (or both) for simply treating a patient with herbs, potions or spells. When wise people gathered together to pay respect to the nature spirits, they were branded as witches and often dispatched in a horrific manner. No mercy was given to those women who painted their bodies with blue indigo and danced naked under the full moon to honor the monthly cycle that brings forth human life to our planet. Those who chose to utilize the God-given plants to open up the center of the universe and the deepest mysteries of the mind were branded lunatics and locked away forever.

Much of the secret herbal lore that was once an integral part of healing, worshipping and maintaining the balance of the world has been hidden away or 'placed in Spirit', awaiting a time when it could once again be safely brought out into the open.

Now we have begun a new chapter in the book of humankind. We have entered a time, according to prophecies from around the world – such as the Hopi prophecies, the Iroquois prophecy, the

Islamic prophecy mentioned in The Holy Qur'an (particularly the chapters entitled 'al-Kahf', the Cave; and 'Nabaa', The Great News), and the prophecies connected with the Aztec calendar – when the 'nine periods of hell' will give way to a 'period of thirteen heavens', as the Aztecs would say. This period is heralded by the return of the ancient art of using herbs to heal those of us in need – through treatments that not only address the physical body but also correct the imbalances that exist in our mental, emotional and spiritual beings.

We will once again remember that we are not just physical beings; that each of us comprises many levels, each one interacting with the other parts of the self. If any one of these levels is affected, then all will be affected, and it is only by treating our illnesses on all levels that we will be able to bring complete health to our bodies and to the Earthmother, for we are all one.

Introduction

Several years ago, just before my family and I were to go back to my native America for a visit, I developed one hell of a sinus infection. Until then I didn't know that so much stuff could be expelled from the nose in any given lifetime, let alone in just a month. Flying at 38,000 feet was not a good thing, either, as it made me nearly pass out from pain.

The condition persisted for the first month in the States and it was only during a trip to the Sierra Nevada mountains, my old home, that I was healed. I honor the vision I was given on that day by the Washoe Grandmothers, and the name that was bestowed on me, BlueFeather, for it was a wise name. Within twenty-four hours I was well on the way to recovery and ate more breakfast than I would ever have thought possible. Although I had cleared many things on the mental, emotional and spiritual levels, it needed also to happen on the physical level before I could move forward.

In the last few years there has been an ever-increasing number of books dealing with herbs and herbal medicine. It is good to see this renaissance of natural healing taking its rightful place in the development of a holistic approach towards health, entwining modern technical advancement with methods that have, for untold centuries, maintained the health and well-being of our ancestors.

It is now time to incorporate a deeper understanding of what makes us unwell – but not just on the physical level: to begin to recognize that most illnesses begin in our emotional, mental and spiritual beings and then manifest themselves as physical.

Many of the herbs covered in this book are used to delve into the etheric world that exists, unseen, all around and inside each one of us; to take that giant step into the unknown to find out who we really are, and what we need to do to heal ourselves and the world we live in.

Much of this work takes courage, as it forces us to face the hidden pollution that lies in our mind and soul and affects the reality of our everyday life, our health and our relationships. No one can be completely cured of their ills unless they engage in a 'weeding of the soul', and that can only happen when we clearly see the issues that hamper our earthly existence, and thus become more loving, selfless and compassionate human beings.

In the world of plants there are the 'Grandmother' plants – those that wash away the stress and confusion that we bring ourselves in this world (see Part 3); and the 'Grandfather' plants – those that bring us insight into the proper way to live (see Part 4). All of these plants have been put here on Earth by the Creator of life so that we may all live in an attitude of respect towards ourselves and all our relations – the insect and animal nations, the plant nations, our brother the wind, our sister the snow, our mother the Earth and our father the sky. Everything that exists in nature is our relative and deserving of our care and respect. There is no dis-ease, no illness, no trauma that cannot be wiped clear through the careful, professional administration of these divine plants. It is the aim of this book to dispel the myths and misinformation that have clouded our minds concerning their use.

WARNING: Many of the treatments mentioned in this book can be dangerous if taken lightly or without a genuine intention to cure ourselves. They were not given to us to be regarded casually or disrespectfully; and to do so would only be to invite mental, physical, emotional and spiritual disaster.

These cures are not about getting high, to block out the world around us; rather, their purpose is to bring forth a new reality that will, in time, bring us back into balance with all life and with ourselves.

PART 1

dis-ease and healing

What makes us sick?

Look around and you will see illness and 'dis-ease' manifesting themselves in every form imaginable. They appear in our children, in our families and loved ones, in the people we live and work with. If we take the time to watch the people who go by us in our daily lives, we will witness an endless variety of infirmities.

The statistics are staggering. In Australia, twenty-nine per cent of the population will develop some form of cancer, and that percentage can be expected to be much higher in areas of the world that have chronic pollution. Not all that long ago cancer was considered to be a disease of old age, and now it has become common among people of all ages. Also, one in eight of us will suffer some form of mental illness in our lives, and I suspect that the level of 'hidden' mental illness makes the proportion even greater. At a time in history when we have at our disposal a miraculous array of medical techniques and technology, more people than ever appear to be succumbing to an ever-increasing list of illnesses.

When I was a child and penicillin was still a relatively new wonder drug, it was envisaged that, by the end of the century, we would have eliminated much of the disease that had always plagued humankind. With the help of new surgical tools, radiation, chemotherapy and a vast collection of new and more powerful drugs, we were going to have the healthiest culture in history. Together with the evolving technical advancements in labor-saving devices, communication and travel, we would have the time and ability to live long, leisurely and educated lives free from the stresses that had taken such a heavy toll on our ancestors.

What happened to that dream? As a society we are more

overworked, stressed and sick of mind, body and spirit than ever before. So what is making us so sick?

Environmental illness

Look at what we have done to the sacred Earthmother, she who brought us up from the mud of creation and nurtured us since the beginning, and you will see one of the primary factors of our condition.

As we continue to dump our filth and toxins into her rivers and streams, her lifeblood, our own veins and arteries become filled with poison-saturated blood. Every estuary that gets drained and filled in to build yet another shopping center or housing project damages the Earth's ability to filter these toxins, and we see our own livers reduce in function or fail as our physiological systems become over-loaded with toxins. Every new agent that we spew into the air cre-ates more congestion, asthma, bronchitis and lung disease in our bodies. As we clear what is left of the rainforests, our kidneys will eventually give up even trying to power the human body. When we see the oceans' ecology collapse and fail to support the richness of life that once flourished there, our minds will become vast waste-lands of emptiness and despair. Everything we do to our Earth-mother we do to ourselves and all other creatures. Her soil is our skin becoming increasingly pock-marked and eroded.

When we learn to respect the Earth and everything on and within it, we will learn to respect our bodies and the bodies of others. One of the best health insurance schemes would be to insure the health and well-being of the Earth.

In monetary terms, every dollar we spend on cleaning up and restoring the proper ecological balance on our planet will come back to us tenfold in a reduction of the cost of medical care. This is no longer a matter of just saving what we have left, for there is sim-ply not enough of the Earth's natural resources left to maintain us and our lifestyle. It is about restoring the air, soil, forests, oceans, streams and rivers so that we may be restored. Clean the air, and we will once again breathe deeply without impairment. Filter out the toxins from our waterways, and our blood will once again run clean and strong. This is the greatest challenge that we face today. We have a choice: we will either renew our promise to take care of the Earth, or we will die.

How can we do this thing that seems so ecologically and economically impossible? We are told that we simply do not have the money or resources to take on such a challenge. Yet I believe that for those who are sick of mind or body, there could be no greater therapy, physical and mental, than to work with the Earth and heal the world around them. Each one of us has the ability to heal ourselves; but we will also need to cleanse the Earth, or only half of the work will be done. Many of us who are sick of mind have become disconnected from our Earthmother and it is only when we realign our relationship with her that we begin to facilitate healing on that level.

We must also strive to re-connect with the spiritual ecology of our world, to understand better those forces that are often unseen in our normal reality but which make up the other half of all that we are. For all things there is a spiritual, or etheric, energy that persists even when the material vessel ceases to exist. Just as we are all bound together within the physical web of life, we are also intrinsically bound by the invisible threads that tie us to our higher selves. Whether you call our combined energy 'God', 'Spirit' or 'cosmic consciousness' matters not, for it is all the same thing.

Just as we value and honor the physical earth and all her glories, we must also bring back the ancient practices of honoring the spiritual essence of our planet and the often unseen entities that make up the spirit world.

These are the plant spirits, the animal spirits, the mineral spirits, the spirits of our ancestors and an infinity of others. Through our ever-increasing connection with the world of Spirit, we shall once again learn to trust the lessons we will receive that will guide us to the most effective means of helping our world, for we have all been given the gifts necessary to bring us into balance and harmony.

Mental illness

The more I see people sink into the dark realm that we call mental illness – that is, slip into the abyss of depression, anxiety, psychosis, neurosis and the countless other symptoms of what indigenous people often refer to as 'the disease of civilization' – the more I am convinced that the way the technological world operates at the moment is the madness and that the ones who have discovered this fact are the ones who are labeled 'crazy'. Many of us have looked at the world and decided to seek the refuge of sanity. To a world that has largely become insane and set out on a path to self-destruction, this appears quite mad.

When we begin to change ourselves in an effort to become self-empowered beings, it is easy to slip into one of the many forms of mental illness. One of the reasons for this is that we are challenging every ideal and value that we have been taught by the world, and in many cases we see the double standards and lies that have become ingrained in our society. At the very moment that we begin to question what road we have taken, and realize that there are many roads to walk on, we start to re-organize our brain and the way we view the world.

One of the first blocks that we encounter when we start our metamorphosis into what I refer to as the Fifth World is usually fear. That is our first great hurdle, and one that literally scares people away from the journey. Many find it easier to take some medication that makes the fear go away than to charge headlong into the terror that accompanies fear.

Those who choose to go through the fear and come out the other side find that fear becomes their strongest ally. From having gone through it, they know that it is all illusionary and they will never fight fear again. Fear is the greatest of teachers and the lesson we learn from it is empowering.

Imagine if you will that fear is like one of those pictures that you have to stare at for a while before the three-dimensional image begins to emerge. Once you have seen the hidden image it is easy to call on that knowledge to find it again, but you must first see through the two-dimensional illustration that you see initially. The previously unseen picture becomes something familiar, like a friend.

One of the reasons we human beings are so often fearful is that we possess a unique quality of mind that is able, unlike any other animal, to question everything. If caterpillars pondered on why they had a sudden impulse to shed their skin for the last time and be encased in a dark shell hanging upside-down from a twig, few would have the courage to proceed and we might never have butterflies. We fear things that are natural and normal for human beings to fear because we question everything, but there are few people in our culture who understand this process as anything but illness. In many ways, encountering fear is an essential ingredient on the road to self-empowerment.

Many of the world's cultures view mental illness as a gift from the Creator bestowed on those who wish to view life differently. Where this belief pattern is ingrained, people who manifest permanent altered states of consciousness lead useful and empowered lives, and are often sources of great wisdom to those around them.

There is certainly a need to develop a wide range of treatments for those who are truly suffering at the hands of mental illness, but we also need to understand the depth of the problem; that disease which manifests itself in the mind often has its roots buried deep in emotional, sexual and spiritual issues, and only by treating it on all levels will we begin to tackle the problem.

The good news is that there are healers, and methods still practiced today, that seem to be able to cure even long term mental illness within a few days or a week and are permanent in their effect. One such treatment, used by the Navajo (Dine) people of the American south-west, is called N'tesh and involves covering the subject with the ash of a grass called Big Bluestem (*Andropogon gerardi*) and reciting a chant that takes up to seven years to learn and twenty-four hours to repeat. When the ceremony is complete, the ash is washed off the body and the ailment is gone. This may seem like just another tale, but it is the truth. It is said that, in the old days, the ceremony would last four days, but since time is running faster these days, it now only takes one.

Many cures can be effected in a day or less, sometimes instantaneously. There are many herbs that, if used properly and with a great deal of knowledge and respect, will work on all four levels: the physical, mental, emotional and spiritual bodies.

One such plant is datura or jimson weed. **Let me stress at this point that all parts of all species of datura are quite lethal if taken even in small doses.** But to the trained healer it can be an invaluable tool in the treatment of many forms of mental imbalance. There is an old saying amongst the Dine that if you are sane it will make you crazy, but if you are crazy it will make you sane. The process of making datura relatively safe is not one that I choose to cover in this book, as it would inevitably lead to someone thinking they can get a quick 'buzz' from this plant and end up as another fatal statistic. The truth is that datura is *never* safe and the spirit of this plant tends to be fairly unpredictable. If the spirit likes you, you might just live, but if he takes a dislike to you or your attitude, he will send you into a world of madness from which there is little chance of escape.

Later in the book we will discuss other plants that, by altering our state of consciousness, help to bring forth issues that lie within our four-layered beings and help us understand how we bring dis-ease and illness upon ourselves. We will learn that, in many cases, one can address the physical ailments that make us realize we are sick, by travelling to different dimensions where the true causes of our malady are formed. That has always been the road of the medicine men, the witches, the *brujo* or *bruja*, (traditional South American or Mexican healer) sages or prophets.

Emotional illness

In many ways, emotional illness ranks as the most insidious and damaging form of illness because the sufferers are often unaware that they have a problem. Most seem to suffer dis-eases which, although not life-threatening at first, manifest themselves down the road as something more serious because the initial cause was never dealt with.

I have lived a long life already and have seen many things, but one peculiarity seems to come up repeatedly. People are often 'labeled' or nicknamed in a way that seems somehow to manifest itself on the physical level and often cause dis-ease.

I knew a man once who had been given the name 'grizzle-guts' by his family. He was a really wonderful, caring and kind man, but you could see written on his face and in his body language that he had a lot of repressed anger that he had never dealt with. He developed liver cancer and died, and I have always believed that this anger went there and killed him in his guts, so to speak. People who are referred to as heartless often die of heart attacks and those who are known as a pain in the ass . . . well, you figure it out.

When we are emotionally ill – and the world seems now to be filled with people who, in some way, are sick emotionally – it is very easy to view everyone around us, or maybe the way our family or friends abused us when we were young, as the problem. The fact is that this is the way we come into the world as we know it; our spirits have not yet grown into emotionally blooming beings, and so we choose the family into which we are to come, and the people around us make the world in a way that will comply with the spirit's need to 'learn the lessons'. If we can look at these childhood experiences in this way, we can find a way to bring forth our emotional growth and free our souls from having to repeat the lesson.

At the heart of healing is the knowledge that we chose the world we were born into and must take full responsibility for what it has brought us. In this way we begin emotional healing.

In many indigenous cultures of the world emotional illnesses such as substance abuse, child or spousal abuse, environmental abuse or societal abuse are treated in a far different and usually much more effective way than in some Western cultures. The role of the psychic healer is to put the subject into a different reality – into the realm of Spirit where the problem can be dealt with 'directly' rather than through the illusionary world of matter, time and space. The shaman knows many ways to induce such a state of consciousness, often including the use of psychotropic plants. Among these plants, which I call the 'Grandfather' plants, are peyote, jimson weed, sage, Syrian rue, several species of salvia and many, many more growing on our abundant earth.

There is a ceremony that originates in West Africa involving a plant called ibogan. It is said that, through the careful administration of this plant, people who have had any form of addiction, particularly drug abuse, are transported back in time to view, scene by scene, every event that helped form their addiction, and by seeing this are able to identify the issues, brought into this world from spirit, that created their abusive behavior. The cure is often complete within twenty-four hours, and very few people who participate ever go back to their old pattern of abuse.

Other forms of altered states that induce emotional healing can be brought about in many other ways, including drumming, dancing, fasting, sleep deprivation, pain, sacred sex, chanting, menstruating, meditating, and flute-playing. As I look over this list I realize that, with the exception of menstruating, I often did all of these things during final examinations, which may explain why I rarely did well in those tests and why students are often seen by the general public as such strange people.

There are still many shamans who can thrust you into an altered state of consciousness simply by touching or hitting you in a certain place. Instantly the world you were viewing is gone and in its place is something different. It is a very strange experience, but the effect is the same: you are in a place where your issues are right out there in front of you and you cannot shift your attention away from them because there are no radios, televisions, video games, or any other forms of escape.

Most people I know in this Western culture of ours have a great fear of this form of healing because they think it will leave them vulnerable or out of control. Such a fear is understandable, because that is basically what happens. In the altered state we lose our ability to control the reality of the physical world and the endless ways in which we fool ourselves and divert our attention from those things that keep us from being the shining lights we are meant to be. We may unleash some deep, dark, sinister being from the depth of our souls and then discover that this thing is us. We may be filled with terror as we leave the only view of the world we have known except in our dreams, but what we are trying to scare to death is our ego, for that is what is at the root of emotional illness.

The ego is the prime mover in our effort to control ourselves and the world around us. For those with emotional illness, the ego receives its power from disempowering others, and in doing so creates disharmony, judgmental behavior and a sense that all our problems come from external forces that are out of our control. This is one of the most insidious of all our illusions: that we cannot control the illusion.

The very cornerstone in the pyramid of learning to develop as a human being is our acceptance that what is happening around us is first generated inside us, on the spirit level, so to speak, and that it is then 'transferred' to the world that we know as the 'real world'. This is a concept that is well understood by those who strive to grow as human beings, and it is a difficult road to follow. Because it is so difficult, there are many people who try to walk this road but few who succeed. For the first signpost on this road says 'Be Responsible for Your Own Reality'. The second says 'Create the Reality Your Heart Wants' and the third reads 'Caution, Fear Ahead'. Many people falter on this highway of life, but with dedication to the truth, self-knowledge and the ability to break through fear, we can all lead emotionally abuse-free lives in the service of our God and all our relations.

Upon my return to civilian life after serving nearly four years in the Air Force (one of those four in Vietnam), I went back to college and became quite interested in psychology. One of my teachers was a man who was a great believer in the theories of the Swiss psychiatrist and psychologist Carl Jung. Jungian philosophy recognizes the power of our subconscious to make manifest in the physical that which has not been dealt with in our spiritual, mental and emotional 'bodies'. (It is interesting to note that much of the work of Carl Jung comes directly from the teachings of the Dine (Navajo) people of the American south-west, with whom he studied and corresponded for many years.)

What, then, was being manifested in my involvement with the horrors of the Vietnam War? How was it possible for such a thing to happen in my life when I was brought up in the idyllic setting of Southern California?

I had what I thought was a good upbringing, in a clean, middle-class environment and with a mother and father who really loved and cared for me. It took me many years to work out the connection, but when I did, my discovery began to change everything else in my life and the way I tried to deal with things. Vietnam was an 'undeclared war', and so, in many ways, were the family dynamics that were in place during my childhood. It was a time when social problems were never discussed, and television portrayed the perfect American family in a constant array of programming designed to make the real families feel cheated. Why wasn't my dad like Ward

Cleaver or Robert Young or any of the other TV dads? And why did my mum look so nice and happy even when I could feel that she was angry. There were, as it turned out, many undeclared wars going on under our roof, but because I did not even acknowledge that they existed, they were projected out into the physical world around me.

People regain and maintain their power and become fully developed human beings by striving to take responsibility for what happens to them, and in doing so, truly free the soul.

Sexual illness

Writing about sex is a bit like rowing a boat on very still waters, trying not to disturb the surface too much. If you row like mad you will have succeeded only in reaching your destination quickly; meanwhile, the scene reflected on the water's surface becomes obscured. If you row too slowly, you will never get anywhere. So I will put my literary oars in slowly, gently, but deeply.

Sexual health depends on a good attitude towards sex and an unconditional love for ourselves, our bodies and our partners. If you are ashamed of a body part or function, it is very likely you will develop some dis-ease in that part of the body, or somewhere related.

The two greatest causes of sexual illness and dysfunction are shame and guilt. Shame over sex and our bodies is usually introduced to children of our culture at a very young age. Infants can surely sense their mother's discomfort at having to breast feed under the gaze of an intolerant public. Since breasts are primarily for feeding infants, to put shame on that act is to put shame on every human breast on the planet. It says, 'Put away and hide that which God gave you so that you may nourish your children.' To be detached from the breast and our mothers' warmth and nourishment is to begin the first steps on the path towards separation from our Earthmother and thus towards sexual illness.

This applies to any other part of the body that shame attaches itself to. There must be a lot of shame out there, considering the ever-increasing number of shame-related dis-eases such as uterine and prostate cancer, breast, skin, testicular and bowel cancer. I am not saying that any of these dis-eases can't be manifested through poor diet, genetic (ancestral) factors or many other causes. It is only an observation that many people I have known have suffered cancer in parts of the body that, on the psycho-sexual level, they felt shame about.

Guilt is the fuel that keeps the ember of shame glowing until at last it ignites into a wildfire of sexual dysfunction and illness. The more you try to suppress it, the longer it smolders. It's like trying to sit on water to make it disappear. You only get deeper in it.

Guilt is the means by which others gain control over our lives. No matter who it is who is dishing out the guilt – whether it is the church, our parents, our siblings, other relations or people we deal with in our daily lives (including the government), the reason is always the same. Guilt is meant to disempower you, and it is the oldest trick in the book.

The best way of overcoming guilt is firstly to stop listening to those who seek to control you and listen to what your heart is telling you; and secondly to understand that in the world of Spirit there is never judgement of our actions. God does not see the good or bad in us. God only sees. The only being truly judging us is our-selves. What other people say about us cannot affect us if we are strong in honoring the decisions we have made.

Know that your body is a good and clean thing, and that sex is one of the ways we have been given to express our feelings of love for another. It is the closest many of us get to re-uniting our spirits here on earth, and it needs to be recognized as a sacred act, one not to be taken lightly. There is an old saying that I just made up, which says 'If you want to pray together, lay together.' This, of course, applies only to consenting adults.

Our society has a funny way of, on one hand, shoving sex down our throats at every conceivable opportunity, figuratively speaking, while, on the other, condemning those who engage in it. In most indigenous cultures, sex is viewed as a normal and natural part of life, and it is the wise grandmothers who teach the sacredness and importance of our sexual being to the young ones. And it is the grandmothers who sit around late at night doing their crafts who tell the 'dirtiest' jokes, for they now see the humor in it all.

The body, it is taught, is our sacred temple and we must honor it. It is that which brings us life, nourishment and pleasure and let us thank the Creator for such a gift. But let us also not mistreat it, for it must carry us far if we are to get anywhere.

You could say that there's sex and then there's spiritual sex. The difference has more to do with intent than content. Whereas ordinary sex has its basis within the physical realm of gratification, spiritual sex is all about the sharing of spirit and comes from the heart and soul rather than the loins. It is an honoring of the Goddess who dwells within and the God who dwells throughout. It is two beings meeting in the light of our perfection rather than the darkness of guilt and shame.

Let me just say that once you've had spiritual sex, there's very little desire to go back. It's no wonder that God's name keeps coming up during good sex, for that's one of the things we can do in our physical bodies that brings us closer to God and the spiritual world. If done for lust, power, disempowerment, shame or guilt it will only take you further away.

Spiritual illness

Spiritual illness is, I believe, at the core of most (if not all) illness, dis-ease and 'accidents'. As our soul moves through the evolutionary journeys of life, we bring along with us certain natural flaws in our soul character. As we progress, with each lesson we rid ourselves of more and more of the primal drives that rule our physical lives and come closer to achieving that consciousness where we are closer to living through love than living through fear. When we learn to love ourselves and all others, and become a clean, clear shining cylinder through which we channel the unconditional love of the Creator, we achieve Christ consciousness. There are many who walk on the world today who have achieved this spiritual alignment with their physical bodies and become bright lights in a very dark world.

Everywhere there are signs and prophecies that the time has come when a great spiritual sickness will envelop the world and its darkened form will blot out much life and light. At the core of each one of these predictions is the belief that a 'saviour' will come just in time and save humanity from the anti-Christ, as it is termed in the Bible. But if Christians, Jews, Muslims, Native Americans and many other groups believe this to be true, then just who will appear? If Jesus returns, then the Jews, Muslims and everyone else are going to be very upset. If Mohammad descends to Mecca, all hell will break loose, so to speak. And if the Pale One returns to the Native Americans, then the Bureau of Indian Affairs is going to have a very red face.

The fact is that the anti-Christ is already here – not in the form of an individual, but as a way of life that has become like a great pestilence across the Earth. It rapes our Earthmother of her beauty and abundance and ejaculates into her the seed of hate, lust, greed, disempowerment, prejudice, intolerance and the belief that this can continue forever.

The Hopi people have told us that there will be a time when everything that you buy or sell will have the 'mark of the bear' on it, and that people, too, will begin having these marks. It would be like a plague on the land and come close to destroying all people.

When I first heard the Hopi prophecies I interpreted them as meaning that somehow the Russians would win a war against America and all products and many people would literally have a bear (the Russian emblem) displayed. This prompted me to move to the

Sierra Nevada mountains and to learn to become self-sufficient. It wasn't until a friend of mine and I were out walking in the woods one day that I discovered the truth. He was looking at a tree and mentioned that there must be a pretty big bear in the neighborhood. That tree had the mark of a pretty big bear because the scratches on the tree were at least eight feet off the ground. Of course! When a bear marks its territory, it leaves large vertical scratches on the trees in its region to let others know how big it is. There was no mistaking the similarity between the 'mark of the bear' and bar codes.

If we take this one step further, we might speculate that the 'sign of the beast', which the Bible talks about, is all about bar codes as well, as I would assume that both bears and lions leave similar marks on trees. This is how the dark forces have tricked us all. We are waiting for someone to come along and try to destroy us and someone else to clean up the mess, when all along we are destroying ourselves and the only mother we have ever really been born from – all in the name of a strong economy based on the exploitation of the poor and the oppression of all those who have yet to succumb to the 'sign of the beast'. And if we wait for some saviour to bail us out, it will be too late. What we need to do is bring in the energy and teachings of all those sons and daughters of God that have come to us always in time of need and taught us the way to be better human beings. We then put our efforts into becoming as close to that which I prefer to call the Christ consciousness, and become one with our Creator and our Earthmother. Then the Earth will truly become a paradise.

The greatest sickness we are experiencing right now is spiritual illness. We see it everywhere around us, even firmly embedded in many 'religious' movements of the day. Wherever one group of people calls for the oppression or murder of those who do not follow the popular dogma, there is spiritual illness. Any time someone thinks they are better than another because they follow a more holy guru, or have different colored skin, a purer heritage or more riches, there is darkness. With every true prophet has come the same message dressed in a different set of clothes. Some have appeared to the Native Americans of North and South America. Others have appeared in Africa, Europe, Asia . . . wherever human beings thirst for truth. But, each time, the message is the same: be kind and loving to yourself and all others. Put yourself over no one. Cure your spiritual illness and you will heal your world. When we once again understand that we are all connected and equal, our spiritual path will be clear and free. If it is judgement day, then we will only be judging ourselves.

We need not give up material possessions but only the blind acquisition of wealth without regard for the well-being of others and those of the next seven generations, as the Cherokee often say. We need not give up our comfort but only the drive to conquer the elements. If we work with them they will provide great comfort. We must eliminate greed and replace it with giving, for in this way we will gain abundance of spirit. This is the road to spiritual wellness, and for those who embrace it there will be great reward.

Why so many people are happy being sick

How can anyone enjoy being sick? It is expensive, inconvenient, quite often painful and eventually it can be fatal. It keeps us from doing our job, creates enormous guilt in some people and rarely seems to make us happy externally. But for so many people to be sick there must be something that we like about it or we wouldn't be sick.

The fact is, it takes hard work to stay fit and healthy. It is not something you can get from a video game, the television, the takeaway shop or in any other quick fix way. Some people become chronically sick because they refuse to look at the root causes of the illness, or because it simply becomes easier not to have to get out of bed any more.

Being sick is not necessarily a bad thing. It tells us in a final and most direct way, through our bodies, that we need to stop doing whatever it is we are doing and look at our stuff. It often gives us a clue as to where the real disturbances lie.

In societies that function for the benefit of all, this is recognized and honored for the wisdom and insight that illness can bring, not only to the person who is sick, but also to the other people affected, and adequate time and space are allotted to all concerned to facilitate a complete cure.

Within the Cherokee culture, people with chronic mental, physical, emotional or spiritual sickness were allowed to enter the 'White Village', a place that served as both a training ground for those in the priesthood and a refuge for those who came to seek help, such as those who were sick or had committed a crime. In this monastery-like setting, sick people were truly cared for on all four levels, and no judgement on them would ever be made. It was not uncommon for people to spend a year working through the issues that created the dis-ease, after which they would return to their own village to resume their normal life with the support and encouragement of all.

It is a good guess that, unless we change much of how we conduct ourselves as a world community, more people are going to be happier being sick than well, for there are many who feel safe when they are sick. Although it can be an isolating experience for some, it can also be a good excuse to just get away from everyone. If we're lucky we get sympathy, and if we don't we have validation of our belief that nobody really cares.

Understand that sickness can also be a sign of a great clearing taking place on one or more levels, usually all. Often when we are discharging great quantities of bodily fluid such as mucus or vomit, it means that, on the physical level, we are cleaning up and eliminating unwanted pathogens. On the etheric level it can also indicate a cleansing process, just as with the sinusitis attack that I described earlier in the introduction. That is one of the reasons why herbal treatments are superior to allopathic medicines and drugs. Herbs afford us the opportunity to aid our bodies and souls to naturally combat dis-ease without simply masking the symptoms.

Some drugs can certainly help ease the symptoms and supply a level of comfort to the patient, but there always seems to be a price to pay down the track. One of the costs can be the fact that you may not be allowing yourself to fully accept the lessons that can be learned from being sick.

When do we start getting better?

Now for the good news. We are already starting to get better, for understanding is the first step towards good health and well-being.

The bad news is that we will probably see more illness over the coming years than we have ever seen before, because we have much clearing to do. Our hospitals are rapidly becoming the last place you would want to be when you're sick, for the simple reason that sickness resides there.

Also, more exotic dis-eases are appearing every year and many old ones are returning from the past with immunity from antibiotics. This is forcing the medical establishment to learn new techniques that have their roots in the past and that bring together the medical lessons from other cultures and other times.

Only now, through our miraculous technology, can we bring back together the medical and spiritual knowledge acquired over centuries and use it to accomplish the greatest task that has ever faced human beings: to rebuild our world and ourselves. We can begin to see this in the songs of the youth and their dedication to saving the planet, their thirst for truth and knowledge and their desire to establish a world of love and understanding between all people. They have the most to lose and the most to gain.

Many of our young people feel isolated and alienated from the very culture that has brought them life and 'comfort'. They sense a purpose for being here but don't know what that is. They are, to coin a phrase, all dressed up with nowhere to go. Often they feel their parents don't understand them, the workforce doesn't want them and the world won't listen to them, but listen we must for they are the voice of our conscience, our ancestors and our spirit guides, all come to Earth to lead us out of this madness and emptiness. We must ease them gently into their power with the strength of our love for them, and then we must be ready to follow them, for they, in turn, will lead us to great heights of personal and planetary healing.

We see many young people risking injury and freedom to save what is left of our decimated rainforests, while others are working to re-forest the world. Before long we may plant more trees than we destroy. There is also a growing number of people risking life and property to save the oceans of the world from utter collapse, breathing hope into the lungs of our Earthmother and fighting those who seek to destroy her. American Indian prophecy predicted the return of Earth's army, The Rainbow Warriors, and they are here fighting for our right to live on a clean planet. The path is filled with hope.

For those who wish to restore the Earth by growing and harvesting herbs I can tell you that it is a road to self-discovery – whether you do it to provide yourself and those you love with good medicine in times of need or you do it to fulfill a deeper need to re-unite with the Earth's elemental forces and find a peace of mind by interacting with the ebb and flow of life.

The deeper one goes into this world, the bigger it becomes. It is an infinite thing, worlds within worlds and lives upon lives. We are starting to get better because we finally want to get better and will do our work on all four levels. We will diligently weed our gardens of guilt, shame, hypocrisy and greed and plant the seeds of tolerance, compassion, understanding and abundance for all. So mote it be.

How do we maintain good health?

The simplest way to answer this question is with the following list:

- Laugh a lot, particularly at yourself.
- Keep busy when it's necessary and do nothing when it's needed.
- Do most things in moderation and some things in excess.
- Keep a positive outlook, even when the crap hits the fan.
- Remember that, like plants we need crap to grow.
- Too much crap is not good for plants or people.
- Feed your body and your mind.
- Eat well, drink lots of liquids and get plenty of exercise.
- Sometimes eat bad food, drink wine and lie on the couch.
- Never smoke anything bad for you.
- Never wear clothes when you don't have to.
- If you have a good voice, sing to honor God.
- If you don't have a good voice, sing to get even.
- If you drink and drive, you're a bloody idiot.
- Think of others before yourself, but don't forget yourself.
- Self-control is not always a good thing. Lose it sometimes.
- Destroy destructive things and nourish nourishing things.
- Get up before the sun and spend an hour meditating.
- Stay up late and don't get out of bed before noon.
- Have lots of sex when you're young.
- Have lots of sex when you're older.
- Never stop learning in life and about life.
- Read this list every day and add to it if necessary.

PART 2

working with herbs

The true nature of plants

Most of us are around plants at least some of the time, and some of us may interact with plants all day, without giving a conscious thought to these life forms that produce our oxygen, filter our pollution, hold our earth together and shade us on a hot day.

Few people in our society have any idea of the complex nature and character of plants. Were this to change, so, too, would our world. For plants are alien to our animal way of thinking, yet the evolutionary path of our souls is the same: to honor God by becoming godly ourselves. To show unconditional love for all things as God shows unconditional love towards us. The plant world, being the eldest child of God, so to speak, has progressed along this path a greater distance and will teach us the secrets of the journey if we will only listen.

How do we listen to plants, you may ask. The answer is simple. Since the reality of most plants is much slower than ours we must first slow ourselves down in order to hear what they have to say. To plants, we must seem like a blur of hectic activity, running around at break-neck speed, hardly aware of the 'real' world around us. If we slow down our actions and thoughts we will begin to receive a much different view. In this section I will try to describe to you the true nature of plants.

On the physical level plants and humans are not all that different. Like animals, plants are made up of cells that have diversified into many different types to serve the various functions that define life. There are support cells that hold the structure up; a digestive, nervous, hormonal and sensor system; and a 'brain' to coordinate all of these activities. The plant brain is not centralized like ours, but is contained in each cell of the plant, enabling each cell to communicate with every other cell within its body and the bodies of every other member of its species. In other words, every cell within a red clover plant can 'talk' to every other cell within every other red clover plant in existence.

There is also communication going on between species, when required or desired. Plants often send hormonal signals to other plants in their area to warn of insect infestations, disease or timber-cutters. Upon being signalled they can begin to produce defenses to ward off pests and disease. But since they are relatively immobile, plants have no defense against timber-cutters but to remove their life force and allow it to incorporate into remaining members of the species regardless of distance. Some people regard this life force as part of the plant deva. In other words, when you pull a weed or cut down a tree you do not send that plant's soul to heaven or kill it as we view death; you merely shift the life force into the species soul. With care you can learn to help the plants remove their life force before you actually 'kill' them. In this way you strengthen your connection with that particular species. This knowledge has kept me guilt free although I have dispatched literally millions of plants over the years and have put chainsaw to tree on many occasions while hardly shedding a tear. To take life in a responsible way is the nature of Human Beings.

On the mental level, plants really have it together. There is no madness amongst plants because they are utterly connected to the bigger picture. They question nothing and ask very little of life except life itself. They live for the sake of living and serving all other life, whether that other life threatens them or not.

Just as no two plant species are the same, so it is with the spirit or deva of each species. Some have similar natures, just as there are people of similar character. Most are exquisite in their ability to help us mentally and physically in times of need but other devas can quite literally steal your 'will' or mind.

When I was travelling through South America many years ago I came across a man who, I was told, had great powers but had lost his mind to a rather insidious looking vine that grew in the forest. It was said that the fruit of this vine had the power to increase the power of any *brujo* or *bruja* to almost unlimited proportion, the down side being that if you did not already have sufficient power to master the plant deva, *it* would become *your* master. The man standing in front of me, who just a year ago had been regarded as a great *curandero* (or healer), was now nothing more than a puppet of a human. He showed no emotion, no anger, no anything, and was able to go through his daily routine like some type of zombie. In the end he was arrested and put in a mental institution after he stabbed a young lady with a knife. The slightly wounded lady said that her attacker had had no expression on his face nor any real strength in his arms and seemed to be acting without any control over his own body. From this and many other experiences with plants I am certain that there are plants that have a very malevolent quality to them and must be avoided. The vast majority, however, are filled with a love of life and our world.

Each plant species is, then, an entity or being, with each individual plant within that species being an interconnected part of the whole. Each plant acts as the eyes, ears and nervous system of the deva. Later we will learn how to help plants 'relocate' their life force when they are weeded out or harvested, but for now be content to know that this deva, or mental/spiritual body of a plant does indeed exist.

Within each plant species there is also the emotional body and once again all individuals within the species are interconnected. The medium through which all are linked is vibrational and has a very powerful influence on the planet and the individual. Each radiates at a different frequency and we find that this vibration can make significant changes in the way we view the world. By learning to feel these vibrations we can then ask for healing on the emotional level and accept the unconditional love that is freely given. Hugging a tree can often be a good step towards entering the world of emotional healing.

For those of you who are a bit self-conscious, try leaning against a tree in your backyard for at least half an hour and see if you don't begin to experience some type of emotional shift. Lying on the grass can have the same effect, as any well-adjusted dog will 'tell' you. Children, of course, know this from an early age and it is only after repeated warnings not to touch any plants because they might be poisonous that they begin to move away from their inborn connection to all things. Without the vibrational influences of plants we begin to lose our own emotional foundation, as is evidenced in the inner cities and high-rises. There is a reason why people work and live better in an environment that contains healthy plants. These not only filter the air and give good clean oxygen in return; they also help filter our emotional waste and bring us compassion and the cleansing of our emotional body.

I was told once, as I stared at the grandeur of a stand of redwood trees in Northern California, that those trees were the evolved spirits of humans who chose to come back and spend a lifetime offering prayers of thanks to the Creator, with outstretched arms and heads held high. This is the spiritual quality of plants. Their life is lived far more through the spiritual body than the body we see and recognize as a tree, a shrub or grass. This is their source of unconditional love and understanding of the 'bigger picture'. Since many healers specialize in healing by entering the world of Spirit to find the 'true' cause of an illness and correct it, they call on the spirits of certain herbs, or a spiritual 'ally', to facilitate travel into these other dimensions.

The ability of plants to heal our spiritual bodies is what a lot of this book is about. We have almost lost the link that we have had with plants since the dawn of humanity and in doing so have come close to severing our connection to the spiritual world because we have been led to believe that we must rise above everything else and dominate the planet.

Now, we are beginning to see what has happened to us as we have cut ourselves off from the call of our spiritual beings and come to disregard the spiritual connection with our plant relations. Many people are returning to the old ways of honoring the spirit world through their dedication to and knowledge of the plant world. Know that the devas are here to help us heal on all four levels.

The history of herbal use

There is already a plethora of books on the shelves today that will give you a concise history of herbal use, starting probably with the Chinese and European/Mediterranean chronology and herbal lore. There is a widely held belief that herbal medicine has a relatively short history dating back 6000 years and that before that time it was a matter of hit or miss. It has not been until fairly recently that evidence has begun to emerge that the use of plants for medicine might go back as far as 100,000 years. Still, this is not quite accurate, for the truth of the matter is that most animals use some types of herbs to facilitate their own healing without anybody ever having to tell them what is wrong or how to fix it. Healing is an innate part of our evolution and there is a good chance that it predates mammalian life.

Plants are very good at communicating with most animals, but in our hurry to become civilized we lost the knack of receiving such communication. When an animal gets sick it knows intuitively how to alter its diet or which herbs to ingest to make it feel better. The widely held notion that this has been a trial-and-error type of affair is total rubbish. Animals are guided to the right herbs simply by being connected and listening on all levels.

For humans it has been the same. Once, when a new illness or unknown disease struck a community, there would be those who would communicate with the spirit world and ask for a cure or treatment and it would usually be provided. Effecting a cure was rarely done by experimenting with different herbs; it was simply a matter of bringing the cure back from Spirit.

There are many stories about how this communication takes place. One of my favorites is about a Native American who started up a practice in New England during the early 1800s. When a typhus epidemic hit the area, it is said that Dr Pye had a vision in which the spirit of a plant told him that its leaves would be of benefit for the condition. Although the root of this plant, gravelroot (*Eupatorium purpureum*), was known to him as a cure for gall stones and urinary complaints, he had never used the leaves. These turned out to be quite successful, due in part to their ability to induce profuse perspiration. This herb is now also called Joe Pye weed.

Any traditional healer will tell you that it is the spirit or deva of a plant that comes to our aid when we ask for it. As we move up the evolutionary ladder and become more complex beings, there are always new and effective herbs that will bring us back to good health. The simpler the organism, the simpler the cure. Most likely we have been using herbal remedies since before we crawled out of the ocean, and there is a good chance that we always will.

Learning to recognize herbs

It was not too long ago that most people knew at least a little bit about the recognition of herbs. It was a craft that was most often handed down by our grandmothers, who in turn had learned it from their grandmothers. It was a sacred thread that bound together all parts of the society and kept us connected to each other and our Earthmother.

This knowledge was the culmination of a thousand generations of herbal craft and lore, and was shared wisely and freely. Upon the advent of synthetic medicines, many based chemically on natural agents but lacking the vibration and balance of their organic counterparts, we moved ever farther away from our source of the earthly association that had kept us grounded. Now, the traditional teachers have all but vanished and the thread is broken. Very few of us recognize the very herbs we walk upon in our daily lives. This might be a good place to begin learning about the world around us again.

Unless you have a very cooperative herbalist friend, it might be best if you first go to a good book store (second-hand book stores are often the best) and find a little book on weed identification. Many such books are well illustrated, making it easy for the reader to recognize a particular plant. Hopefully you will also find references in the book to the medicinal properties of certain weeds, and you might be surprised at how many of the plants listed are growing right under your feet.

Spend a few days looking at the pictures, then take some time out in the garden to acquaint yourself with the many varieties of weeds around your property. If you are a very thorough weeder or have no property to patrol, you may have to go to a friend's house or the local park to do your investigation. It is sad that many of us are inhibited about wandering around a public or even private place looking at the ground and perhaps getting down on our hands and knees to have a closer look at natural things. You will probably be asked if you have lost something of value, and you may respond by saying, Yes, we have all lost a thing of value: the time and patience that it takes to look at small things, and the beauty in these. Fortunately we are no longer subject to being burned at the stake, but we are still vulnerable to ridicule.

Within a few short weeks, providing you have not been committed, you will find that at least half of the weeds you have been struggling with in the garden for years are actually herbs that are of some benefit. What's even spookier is that in a few years you will see a pattern, and it can provide you with a little insight into what may be happening to you healthwise before you develop any symptoms.

Often, when I visit someone's home, I will take a quick look around the garden to see what weeds are growing. Plants, being much more in the spiritual world than we are, know when we are heading towards illness long before we begin to manifest any symptoms – when the illness is still in the spiritual, mental or emotional stages. It is therefore possible to begin treatment with the plants growing around you before the problem becomes major, if you know what to look for. It is a great mystery to me how 'weed' seeds always seem to find their mark but it is a confirmation of the interconnectedness of all things, including wind, water and all our relations who spread the seed of knowledge and insight.

Becoming a good herbalist, sorcerer, witch, *brujo,* healer or self-empowered human being is a long process, but it is worth the journey. By marvelling at the preponderance of the small you will open yourself up to a world that has no boundaries. In learning to recognize herbs and plants that benefit us we re-establish the thread of life that reunites us with our past and future.

A simple lesson in intuitive herbalism

Intuitive herbalism requires a little more effort and perhaps a bit more courage for it involves going some place where plants are well labeled, such as a nursery or botanical garden. It may be helpful to have a notebook and pen handy for taking notes if you desire.

Once you have arrived it is most important to put yourself in the proper frame of mind by whatever means you choose. Rid your mind of everything except your willingness to be guided by the plant devas. Once you feel relaxed and receptive, begin walking around slowly, looking for something indefinable that appeals to you rather than for what looks good. It can be something that catches your eye, but you must use all your senses. What is the feeling around the plant? Does it feel warm in some way or do you get a sensation of 'oneness' within its energy field? You may not get it right away.

Since many nursery plants had their origins in herbal use long before they became ornamental specimens for decorative purposes, it is highly likely that the plant you have found an affinity with was once, or still is, used medicinally. If so, and your intuitive powers are good, you may find a connection between the uses that herb has and something that may be, or is, coming up for you. If not, that plant may have some connection with your childhood or past life, or you may find some other, more esoteric connection such as flower essence or vibrational comparability. Is there something about that plant that reminds you of yourself?

If learned properly and with the right intent, this process can be a valuable tool in our inner search for healing through truth about ourselves. Please do not interpret this to mean that you should in any way begin a herbal treatment using the plant or plants you have chosen. This can be a dangerous and sometimes fatal mistake.

WARNING: It is always best to seek the opinion of a trained, skilled medical practitioner or healer before launching into any form of self-treatment, unless you have considerable experience.

It is important, also, not to be too literal in the interpretation of the information you get. Remember that achieving the right state of mind while receiving and interpreting the 'signs' will help clear the path.

A guide to growing and harvesting herbs

We are all, each in our own way, shamans. Many of us deny, hide or run away from our 'medicine', that for which we were born, but we still have that touch of magic and mystery that makes us all shamans. We heal people with a smile or a kind word without recognizing it for what it is. We heal others through a mere touch of reassurance or support and bolster those who are down and out by sharing our abundance.

Growing herbs

When we grow herbs we can take another step forward towards achieving this. Herbs are like children; with the responsibility of starting them comes the more important job of nurturing. It is easy to start seeds, but few people realize the obligation that comes with sowing seeds. What matters is not how many seeds you cast out but how well they get looked after once they have germinated. Growing plants (as with people) requires a commitment of time and energy that does not come easily in our modern world. The growing and harvesting of herbs means spending hours away from the comforts that we have gotten so used to, and becoming more connected to the elemental forces.

SEED GERMINATION

Seeds are the first challenge to work through for the modern shaman. Certainly there are many easy-to-grow herb seeds around and it is always a good idea to begin your journey with something that will not frustrate you right from the beginning. Most of these are started in spring, germinate quickly and will provide you with the basic medicine chest of herbs. But there will come a time when you will want to start growing goldenseal, ginkgo, ginseng, black cohosh or any one of the more difficult and expensive herbs to obtain. Then it will be important to understand a bit more about seeds and what makes them germinate.

Annual plants, that is plants that live for under a year, generally throw off a lot of seed and that seed is quite easy to start if done at the right time of year (usually in late winter or spring). It is important to note that some seed will germinate only if exposed to sun while other seed will sprout only if covered with soil.

In the first year of growth, most biennials (that is, plants that live for only two years) will produce only leaves, before blooming and dying in the second year, but they also throw off great volumes of seed. Most of the seed is fairly easy to sow, although some, like that from angelica, is very short-lived and must be planted soon after collection.

The third group of plants, perennials, includes shrubs and trees. They mostly live for at least two years or longer. Some are fairly short-lived, while others may live for centuries. With long-lived species the germination rate is often very low, while short-lived varieties have a much higher rate. There are some perennial herbs that require many years to germinate and a few others that would challenge the best of us. I know of several that will survive only if grown in the presence of a host species.

DORMANCY

I would like to describe some of the methods that plants have employed to better ensure the survival of their offspring.

For plants that live in areas of extreme cold and snow, there is a distinct disadvantage to having your offspring germinate just before the onset of winter. To keep this from happening such plants have devised many types of germination inhibitors that will allow a seed to sprout only if it has been through a winter. Rain, freezing or a certain period of cold weather will break down these inhibitors, but two winters can occasionally be required to break this type of dormancy. The seeds of goldenseal will often take two cold periods, each of roughly three months, to germinate, and many species of gentian can take up to five years to spring to life.

In areas that are subject to regular fires, such as California, many seeds have only sporadic germination unless they are subjected to heat or fire. The most common way of destroying the inhibitor in these cases is to cover the seed with about fifteen centimeters of pine needles and set fire to the pile. Harsh as this may sound, the results are astounding. Herbs such as kinnikinnik (*Arctostaphylus uva-ursi*) and white sage (*Salvia apiana*) respond well to this treatment.

Again I would recommend referring to seed catalogues whenever you wish to germinate seeds, as it would take an entire book just to cover the individual needs of each herb seed. Instead we will cover the finer points of the subject.

ADDING YOURSELF

No matter how good the herb you buy from the chemist or health specialist, it will not be as good as something you grow yourself. The more of yourself that you put into your plants, the closer their vibrational alignment with your mind, body and spirit. As we work to provide the necessary ingredients to nurture our plants, we nurture ourselves as well and provide a bond that will get the most out of our herbs.

We start this process of bonding when we sow the seeds, so before we put the first seed to earth we must first ground ourselves. I usually employ the Native American technique of 'smudging' or cleansing with the smoke from various plants. This process will be covered later in this book when we talk about some of the plants used in this ceremony. The important thing is not the *content* or *method* of cleansing, but the *intent*. It may only be a moment of silence or meditation, or something that is symbolic of the way you perceive the starting of new life. Whatever you choose, you will find that things always seem to go more smoothly and clearly after a few moments devoted to the clarity of intention.

Upon placing the seeds into the soil and watering them in with a fine mist, it is good to apply a bit of Reiki or some other means of channelling life energy into the seeds. You only have to place your hands five to ten centimeters away from where the seeds lie in the soil and imagine light or energy flowing through your body into your palms, and projecting onto the seed bed or punnet. You will find it helpful for you and the young herbs to do this on a daily basis until the seedlings are well established. Apply this technique whenever you transplant seedlings or young plants and they will recover much quicker.

I always look for ways to tie in whatever I wish to achieve in the way of inner work with the many duties that come along with growing plants. Whenever I weed I think about what it is that I must weed out of my life that stops me growing to my fullest potential. I thank the weeds for showing me what can happen if we ignore them and allow them to take over our growing space, and how it is easier to pull them out when they are small and less noticeable. I find that, if I pull angrily at the weed it struggles more to stay put; but if I carefully and methodically work the weed out of the soil with reason and proper intent, the weed lets go its grip. Pulling the top off a weed and leaving the root will only encourage the root to go deeper underground. This creates twice the work because the next time the 'problem' emerges it will have developed a stronger root that will take twice the time and energy to extract. Once the weed is left for so long that it goes to seed, it infects every other plant around it, and before long there is nothing left but useless weeds.

FERTILIZING

Fertilizing a plant always brings to mind the wisdom that nothing grows without having a bit of 'crap' thrown its way. If we get too much crap we can burn up and die and if we don't get any we simply stop growing. Everyone I know would like to grow more as a human being, but often we complain when Spirit answers the call and applies the shit. It may not smell nice, and it certainly is rarely what we think we want, but if it is viewed as spiritual manure it can be made to seem tolerable. Next time your life seems to be going down the toilet, remember that it is only God putting celestial crap on you so that you will grow.

As you fertilize the herbs in your garden, keep in mind the role you play in nourishing them with the food of the body, the 'holy bread', as it is called. Remember that nothing is permanent. The food of today is the excrement of tomorrow, and tomorrow's excrement will ultimately become food again down the road.

WATERING

Water is the universal cleanser. When we share it with our relations in the plant world, they repay us with a shower of their unconditional love. When shamans water, they give thanks to the spirit of the water and the fact that, without it, all would be a wasteland, all would die. And as the water works its way deep into the roots of the plants we can feel the surge of energy that travels through the entire herbage and radiates into the aura and surrounding area.

In my nursery, every plant in every pot requires water every day. Even on the hottest day, standing in the sun, I feel the surge of energy supplied by each cell as it renews its source of life. Experiencing the water moving through the hose in my hand and out into the soil gives me a small yet moving example of what it must be like for our Creator to be able to dispense the water of wisdom. If our hoses become kinked or clogged, the love and wisdom slows down or is stopped altogether. It is good to keep our spiritual hoses clear and running freely.

We must watch not only that the water is flowing but also that the plant is receiving. There are times when the lowest leaves of a plant will cover over the pot and water is deflected onto the ground and is wasted. The plant will soon thirst and die. As custodian of all the plants you must occasionally prune out foliage that keeps the water from entering the roots. And so it is with God: when necessary for the survival of a life, God will have to 'prune off a few leaves' so that we can absorb the water.

Learn to recognize the signs that plants give out when they are thirsty. When a plant thirsts it will draw moisture from its oldest leaves at the bottom and these will dry out and die. Each time a plant is subjected to drought it repeats this process of drawing the life force from another leaf until there is nothing left to draw from. We, too, are like that. When we are subjected to spiritual drought, we begin to draw the life force out of the leaves of our childhood until there is nothing left to draw upon, and we die. We cannot live without the child-self and it is through drinking the spiritual waters each day that we can hold on to and nourish the things of our child-like ways. You have seen plants that have been neglected. They are bare stems right up to the top where only a few leaves still hold onto life. They seldom, if ever, bloom and if they produce any seed it is usually sterile and will not germinate. We see this in people as well.

In order to begin recognizing the symptoms of under- or over-watering, we need to learn to see truly with our eyes, for these signs are often subtle and confusing and vary from plant to plant. How many times do we look at something without really seeing it? To really see, we must use our etheric, intuitive eyes as well as our physical eyes, and use observation. We must also show sensitivity towards the needs of our plant relations. That is an important lesson to learn on the road to developing as human beings.

There are rules to soul watering and they are simple. When watering herbs remember that each plant is different from the next and you should plant and water accordingly. Also remember that watering is best done before the need arises. Waiting until the foliage is under stress makes it harder for the plant to absorb the water. There is a misconception that it is bad for a plant to be watered in the middle of the afternoon. While it is, for many reasons, more desirable to water in the morning, few plants are damaged by having water on them on a hot day. It is better to water immediately (that means right away) upon spotting a water-stressed plant. If it is in the middle of a hot day, water yourself as well.

Any good gardener will tell you that dry ground is very difficult to water as the moisture tends to run off rather than soak in. Frequent, light sprinkling only encourages the roots to grow near the surface, where they are more prone to damage. It also increases evaporation. Rather, more infrequent but very deep watering will allow the roots to seek the deeper realms where they are safe from the blazing heat of summer.

It takes a long, long time to hand water any area of size. I was once asked by a man whom I will call 'Coyoteman', and who was a great and benevolent teacher, to water his vegetable garden. He took out a pie pan and put it amongst his lettuce plants and instructed me to water the entire garden using the pan as a gauge. When I had filled the pan to the top, which was just over two centimeters deep, there was enough water in it to penetrate into the soil roughly thirty centimeters. The job took a lot longer than I had ever expected and it was an extremely hot day. I had even suspected after the first hour that he had put a small hole in the water pan, but it was intact. Keeping myself wet provided some relief, but there was no shade to be had. As was Coyoteman's habit, he returned just before I finished. Sitting in the shade of his aspen grove he watched me complete my task. When I was done, I walked over, hot and tired, to where he was sitting. I rather expected him to start one of his lectures about some deeper significance of water, but instead he only asked, 'Why didn't you use the automatic sprinkler system?'

I thought it was a test of my ability to stand in the sun for many hours to nurture the plants, but instead it was a lesson in using lateral thinking and not being so pedantic. Getting sunstroke is no way to use your head. Use a sprinkler, and if you don't have one, buy one. Always mulch and water wisely.

POT SIZE

If you're growing plants in pots it is important to be able to see when a herb needs to be transplanted. You will notice the signs: the roots will have outgrown the container, just as we outgrow our 'environment'. When pot-bound, a plant will need to be watered more often, new growth will be stunted and the plant will rarely produce nice flowers. The shamanistic herb grower recognizes these signals and immediately removes the pot, exposing the roots to see if the plant is ready to move to a larger container.

In transplanting it is occasionally necessary to prune constricting roots so as to make room for new growth. If we do not, it is possible that, as the plant increases in diameter, those old roots will eventually cut off the flow of nutrients to the rest of the plant by strangulation. Avoid using a pot that is too big. Take my word for it: small plants get lost in big pots.

SUN

The amount of sunlight a herb receives is of vital importance. Some people believe that herbs grow best in the shade, but this is generally not true. The majority of herbs grow best in full sun. There are many that grow best in partial or total shade, but most prefer at least six hours of direct sunlight each day.

Planning a herb garden can be far more difficult than some people imagine, due to the fact that we, as a society, have forgotten how to notice what goes on in our own backyard. Most people have very little idea how much sunlight hits the different sections of the garden at different times of the year because there is a breakdown in our connection to Mother Earth and her cycles. We often do not see the shifting of our Father Sun as he traverses the seasons, yet it takes only observation to do so. Perhaps we have forgotten how to observe the natural world unless it comes out of the television.

As children we should be taught how the earth and sun move to create the seasons. One hour each month would be enough for anyone to get a grasp on the changing sky patterns, as long as the learning is conducted outside. Taking our children out of the classroom and into the real world would bring them greater wisdom than we can imagine, for if they were to become one with the world they would become one with themselves.

Harvesting herbs

It is said that it is the journey, not the destination, that should bring us the greatest gift. Growing herbs for the experience of nurturing a plant as well as yourself is only part of the process. The growing is the giving end of it, whilst the harvesting is the receiving end of it, and for some the latter is the most difficult. Some people are forever giving to their garden: they find plenty of time to nurture the plants and tend to them in a beautiful way, but somehow never really get around to harvesting and using the end result. For such people, it is easy to give of themselves and their time while it is impossible to receive.

There is a famous picture of an Indian on horseback with his arms outstretched to the heavens, giving thanks to the Creator. There is, however, another symbolic message within the frame: it is that one hand gives to the Creator whilst the other receives.

I was one of those people who could grow the best herbs and vegetables around, yet when it was time finally to harvest the bounty, I would always fall short. I could give until I had nothing left to give, but when it came to receiving, I had a problem.

When we are unable to balance the giving and taking, our lives are unbalanced and this is reflected in areas such as love, friendship and our ability to accept the pure God-love. The shamanistic gardener recognizes this fact and goes to great lengths to develop a ritualistic approach to harvesting. It is an example of how we can correct unbalanced thoughts by having rituals in our lives that reinforce behavior which in turn changes thought patterns. Devising rituals can instill a sense of continuity and pure intent that is hard to duplicate in any other way.

Before we begin the harvest we must make an acknowledgement of our intent. Are we going to use the herbs for ourselves, our family and friends, or are they something we have grown in order to make a little extra money. The answer doesn't really matter, as long as we acknowledge our intent, and there are as many ways to do this as there are people on the Earth. The ritual I use has served me well, so I will pass it on, on the understanding that you accept it only as a guideline. We each have our own way of doing things and it is important that you begin to develop a sense of self-empowerment.

I normally begin the night before the harvest by saying a prayer of thanksgiving for all that has been given to me in this lifetime – good and bad. I ask that the weather be conducive to harvesting the herbs (warm and dry), and that the plants I am about to cut or pull up will aid me and all my relations in healing so that I may be strong in my will and my body so that I may in turn heal others and the Earth. I then address the spirit or deva of the plant or plants I will be working with, and ask them to help me in my work and thank them for the sacrifice they are about to make. I ask for the wisdom to use them properly and the courage to accept the responsibility of receiving the gifts in life. I also ask to be shown in dream or vision the lesson and quality of energy that the herb has to offer, for every herb has something that we can learn from our shared existence on this planet, and they are always ready and waiting for us to take the time to find out what it is. Now, with the formalities out of the way, I can get a good night's sleep and arise to a day of receiving.

The tools you will need for the harvest are simple. I would suggest that, if you do not own a good pair of secateurs, you run out and buy one. This is one of those purchases that can be a lifetime investment, so don't look for the cheapest pair available. It is well worth spending the money and getting something that will last you a long time. This is a personal medicine tool of great value and it will acquire a considerable amount of your energy as you use it, so it is important to look after it. Naturally if you're digging up root crops you will also need a shovel or fork. I prefer the fork because it is easier to dig up the roots without as much damage.

Listening to the plant spirits

Now let us venture out into the garden. When you are standing before the plants you are to harvest, it is best to sit for a while and centre yourself – that is, sit down and quieten your inner voice to eliminate any distracting thoughts.

I find it effective at this stage to concentrate on my breathing. This is the breath of life entering your body and it has remarkable powers when used correctly. Bring each breath in fully through your nose and exhale through your mouth, listening to the sounds around and inside you.

Can you hear the wind? It is the wind that brings us messages from Spirit. Even today in this fast-moving world the wind often sends us signs and insights, sometimes in the form of nature-songs, if we have the ability to hear. Other times the wind works its miracles through devices we have invented that carry vibration through the air, such as television and radio. How many times have you turned on the TV or radio just in time to see or hear something of special significance to your life? This is the way Spirit works in a technological society to bring us the lyrics of the wind. My garden has no television or radio, so I have only the wind as it is in the natural world.

Also listen to the songs of the birds, for they are great allies and messengers bringing us many signs from Spirit. It is easy for Spirit to work through birds because they have such little need of will or ego in their lives. I once had a bird fall at my feet and die to get a message across. As the sun begins to lighten the sky in the early morning, birds sing a special song that actually helps the plants to open their stoma (breathing pores) and start the processes of photosynthesis. They can help further quiet our minds and relax our bodies. When you can begin to pick up the calls of each individual bird it is time to harvest.

If you wish, you may place an offering to the nature spirits before beginning your work. This can be in many forms, such as tobacco (my favorite), corn pollen or flour . . . basically, anything bio-degradable that signifies giving something back for what you are about to receive.

Now you may begin cutting or digging up the herbs. Foliage that is collected can be either laid on a drying rack or hung in small bunches from the ceiling of a well-ventilated shed or room. Root crops are generally washed before being set out to dry, although this is not always the case. The idea is to dry the herbs as quickly as possible so as to avoid molds or fungus forming. The techniques of harvesting are discussed in more detail in parts 3 and 4 of this book.

Now comes the real fun. At the end of the season, when all the herbs have been harvested and put away, it is traditional to have a celebration, as human beings have done for countless generations. This should include music, dancing and a sharing of the abundance that the Earth has provided. It is a time of offering thanks for all we have been given and an opportunity to look at how our lives have been enriched and blessed by the beings with which we share this reality. If we have sown our seed in rich soil, tended and nurtured our garden as we would like to be nourished and cared for, and harvested and shared our bounty with others as the Earthmother has unselfishly provided for us, then it will be a good harvest.

Plant meditation – the golden pathway

There are many methods of meditation used throughout the world but they all aim to achieve the same goal and that is to quiet the mind and relax the body. In a sense it is as close as we get to being fully in spirit while still in the material world. It brings us closer to God, our higher self and the spirits which guide us along our pathway of life.

When I was a child I believed that if you heard the voice of God it would be loud, resounding and not entirely unlike the voice of Charlton Heston. Although I do not discount the possibility that there are those who have heard God speak in just such a way, for me the sound is quieter than a whisper. To hear it one must rid the mind of the seemingly endless chatter that echoes our heartbreaks and conflicts and free the mind of its inner burdens of the material world. For many this is not an easy task, for we have been brought up in a world of noise and distractions at a time when everything seems to be speeding up (it is) and little interval is given for such seemingly idle activity. For those who have yet to experience the calm and tranquillity or meditation, I present you with a technique that may be of some benefit.

Begin by finding a plant in the garden that appeals to you in some inexplicable way. It may be the flower, foliage or just the way the plant 'sits' in the garden. It may even be a house plant that you have tended and nourished for a period. Do not be afraid to use all of your sensory capacities such as touch, smell, sight and intuition. While you are searching for your meditation guide, it is, as always, important to allow yourself to breathe in each breath as deeply as possible and exhale fully. Also become aware of how you are carrying your body and adjust it as you go about the search. Posture is critical in allowing energy (*Chi*) to flow unrestricted through the body. Your posture is a reflection of how much emotional baggage you are carrying around and where you are supporting it. Since disease often manifests in those areas that are bearing the greatest load, it is possible to clear up blockages simply by maintaining a good posture. It is one way that we can help facilitate good health through conscious manipulation of our body. It is the body treating the mental, emotional and spiritual aspects of our lives.

When you have found your plant guide, find a comfortable place to sit next to the plant and begin focusing on the physical features such as form, color and texture. Study the plant carefully, allowing your mind to be free of analysis. In other words, just try to see it without analyzing what you see. This is how our souls see things and it is an important step in seeing spiritually that which we are used to seeing physically.

After you have viewed the plant in this way, begin viewing it as a whole, rather than something made up of individual parts. I find it helpful sometimes to blur my vision (this gets easier for me with age!) until the plant becomes a bit hazy. With some practice you will notice that your ally begins to develop a halo of sorts. This is the aura that is projected by all living things and if the plant is healthy and happy it will take on a golden hue. What you are seeing is the Golden Pathway. When you become adept at seeing the golden light, you may also notice that you will begin hearing a ringing in one or both of your ears. Each species of plant has a particular vibration which can be heard. Some species radiate a very high vibrational sound which is almost outside our auditory range, whilst others emit a low humming sound which for me seems to manifest itself in the occipital area (the lower back part of the skull). Many large evergreen trees have this type of vibrational quality.

It is during this state of receptivity that you will begin to experience an expansion of the Golden Pathway until it starts to merge with your own aura. In reality, we are always connected to everything else, but it is during meditation that we can actually experience this phenomenon taking place. In a world where this type of reality is the exception rather than the rule, this can be considered an altered state of consciousness and like all forms of altered consciousness it takes time and patience to master. Do not be discouraged if you don't get anything right away, for there is great benefit in simply trying. In a society which has largely cut itself off from these types of activities – or, rather, lack of activities – it is understandable that many people find this difficult to learn. Do not get frustrated or lose patience with yourself. We all have our own pace at which we travel through this life and you must not compare yourself with others.

You do not have to restrict this type of meditation to one plant at a time, as it can be just as effective to view a natural setting. It can also be done with rocks, crystals, animals and many seemingly lifeless objects that are endowed with their own energy fields. This is an opened eye form of meditation, having many variations that will suit everyone.

It may take you some time to establish a method that works for you, but it will be well worth the effort. Be diligent in your quest and do not forget that we are here to learn. Also, remember that, as with many things in life, it is the intent rather than the content that is important.

Herbal spells, charms and amulets

At the outset, I feel it necessary to offer a few words of wisdom that I have collected over the years.

Attempting to have control over other people is never the object of projecting herbal spells. This goes against every principle of shamanic practice and flies in the face of the moral obligations that come with any type of spiritual work. The only objective is to work in The Light for the benefit of all our relations and to work in the service of God. Many people begin on this road with the best of intentions but, without the conviction of heart and the ability to use these powers wisely, they find themselves seduced and conquered by the powers of Darkness without even being aware of it. Only when we operate in a clear and heartfelt way to find the hidden 'monsters of the Id' that lie within each of us will we succeed in manifesting true power over our own lives. That is the objective: not to have control or power over our lives or the lives of others, but to have personal power within our lives.

Please do not think that personal power happens overnight. It is a lifelong challenge that takes courage and conviction. We need to look at every issue presented to us and vanquish the obstacle that defeats many people along the way: the ego. It is only by working without ego that the path of the heart remains open and able to channel the limitless power of the Creator.

As with all activities of a spiritual nature, one must be centered and focused, and once again I recommend meditation as the key to this state of being. It is important that, before beginning the preparation of any herbal spells, charms or amulets, we have clear intent and objectives, and it is through meditation that we can best achieve this. If you find that anger, retribution, lust, greed or any other negative feelings come up about the purpose for making any power tool then it is best to stop before you even start. Such motivations will only serve to bring you a great deal of grief and possibly hurt a number of other people in the process.

Throughout this book I will describe ways that may bring you abundance, love, health and well-being. For each one of the following plants I will share with you methods of working with the physical and etheric powers that are within all things. Some of these herbs will, by mutual consent, become your friend and ally, while others may not feel at all comfortable for you to work with. Plants, like people, have their own identity and personality. Some will be conducive to our own personality and some will not. You may also find that some will work for you and some will not. Once again this is about compatibility of characters and not deficiencies of your nature or intent.

Some people say that working within the mysterious world of magic equates to working with dark forces or even the devil. While it is true there are people who practice these methods in a bad way, which serves only themselves and they can get lost in the darkness, the vast majority of practitioners have only the highest of intentions.

It saddens me to hear fellow Christians saying that herbal alchemy is Satan's work, for they ignore the fact that one of the first Christians, John the Baptist, ran around in the wilderness for many years wearing little more than a skirt made of mugwort (*Artemisia vulgaris*) to keep away the evil spirits. My feeling is that many biblical characters used herbs in similar fashion to ward off negative energy, and to secure happiness in marriage, business and friendships. The very fact that Jesus was given frankincense and myrrh after his birth illustrates that the wise men recognized the power of these herbal products in the cleansing and purification of the etheric body. Even today, Catholic priests practice the ancient art of smudging, that is, using the smoke from smoldering plant resin to purify the church before Mass. These are gifts given to us by the Creator so that our lives on Earth may be enriched, and not the work of the devil.

Let us not be dissuaded from the task ahead by fear, confusion or ignorance. Rather, let us rejoin the common links that once bound humankind as one.

PART 3

the grandmothers

Seven sacred trees

Birch

(*Betula*, many species)

Few trees better represent the clever, resourceful, inventive and utilitarian nature of the native people living in the eastern third of North America than the birch. It conjures up pictures of Native Americans gliding peacefully across clear tranquil lakes in a birch bark canoe, going home to the birch bark-covered wigwam carrying a day's catch of trout stored in a birch bark box.

For the people living in the vast birch forests of America the bark of this relatively common tree was responsible for an incredible array of goods useful in everyday life. Objects such as baskets, storage containers, fish traps and even coffins and burial shrouds were made from the bark of this resilient tree.

So waterproof and indestructible is this material that even today it is not unusual for archaeologists to dig up an Indian relic made from birch that is hundreds of years old and still intact. Even leather that is tanned in birch sap is heavily resistant to rotting.

Thin strips of birch bark were also used like parchment paper and often bore secret chants, or were made into calendars for recording daily events throughout the year, or for drawing pictographs and a form of hieroglyphics. Contrary to popular belief, many Native Americans possessed the ability to read and write long before the arrival of European explorers and settlers.

Torches were made by rolling the pliable bark into a cone shape and it is said that these would burn all night.

Possibly the least-known use of the birch was in the fashioning of a scalpel-like tool from a portion of the leaf bud which served to scrape off cataracts from affected eyes. On second thoughts, the most obscure use was in the making of an enema syringe which also used river rushes and deer bladders; it was, of course, disposable after each use.

You might also be surprised to find out that the heated bark from birch trees was once wrapped around fractured or broken bones to keep them immobilized once set, as the bark became quite rigid after cooling.

PHYSICAL ASPECTS

Birch trees will grow to anywhere from ten to thirty meters high, depending on species. Most have a graceful weeping form which makes them invaluable in softening any landscape, although their strong, shallow root systems make them an unlikely candidate for lawn planting. Many varieties have striking autumn foliage while during the spring and summer the small, delicate and

often finely-toothed leaves have an attraction all their own. One of the most striking features is, however, the bark which in most cases is white or silver. The bark often peels away in layers, exposing the beautiful yellow-to-orange inner bark. Male and female flowers are borne on the same tree. Male flowers hang down in long catkins while the female flowers produce woody cones that stay on the tree through the winter. The trees are fairly fast-growing in the right conditions and tend to get much taller than they are wide.

Birch trees are tolerant of most soil conditions, as long as they have adequate water. They are not drought resistant and if affected by dryness will show signs of stress in the leaves, which become dry and brown around the margins. The leaves are often host to aphids. These and the honeydew that they produce can make a mess of the paint job on your car so it is best to plant birches away from the driveway. Honeydew also increases the chances of fungal diseases damaging the appearance and health of young trees. All do best in full sun and appreciate a monthly feed with a mild fertilizer. In areas that have poor soil the roots have a tendency to travel serpent-like along the ground until they find a pocket of richer loam.

MEDICINAL ASPECTS

Medicinally the birch tree has been just as generous. Europeans and Native Americans all discovered the ability of birch bark to treat successfully conditions such as gout, rheumatism and urinary tract infections. The Russians preferred their birch bark soaked in vodka and administered in a tincture for the treatment of liver and gall bladder ailments and as a blood purifier. In a recent Russian medical journal birch was reported to be extremely effective in healing anything from superficial to cavernous wounds. Amerindians (a relatively new name for Native Americans) employed every part of this tree in treating a multitude of maladies. The bark was known to be useful in treating headaches, arthritis and sore muscles and in easing cold and 'flu symptoms well before it was 'discovered' to contain high levels of methyl salicylate, the active ingredient in aspirin. It was also gargled for mouth ulcers and skin eruptions, to clear milky urine and for a variety of stomach problems.

The sap, which is similar in taste to maple syrup, was employed for consumption and brewed into vinegar. The leaves were found useful as a diuretic and to treat dysentery. The roots and twigs were most often boiled down and the liquid added to other less appetizing herbs to improve the taste. One of the favorite teas of the Iroquois was made by simply decocting (boiling in water) the twigs. Finally, the seed cones, which persist through winter, were burned and the smoke inhaled for menstrual pain and also as incense.

I have found little usage of this herb amongst traditional Chinese healers, even though there are native species. I would suspect, judging from other Chinese herbs, that it probably tastes too pleasant to be of any use to them!

SPIRITUAL ASPECTS

You can tell a lot about the spiritual aspects of most plants simply by how they look to the eye, how they feel to the soul and what physical healing effects they have.

For most people the healing effects of the birch come from the way in which the branches appear always to be in a relaxed state, hanging gracefully almost to the ground, as if returning some of the energy that is acquired from the Earth. We get a sense of balance and equilibrium through this feature and can use this energy to bring us closer to a balance in our relationships. If our relationships seem always out of balance then we may find that, by reaching out to the birch in meditation or contemplation, we are better able to understand the need to create a balance within ourselves if we are ever to be successful in our relationships with others. There can be no true love of others until we learn to love ourselves.

The second lesson we find is shown in the bark of the tree. Do you see how the bark peels away from the trunk with every season? This is how our soul grows with age. The layers that have protected the life force of the tree pare away when they have served their purpose. We, too, outgrow our emotional bark and our spiritual growth depends on our shedding these old layers so that we continue to expand. If we are not nourished we do not grow, and if we do not grow we cease to live. You may find a very cleansing quality in the aura of the birch, enabling you the strength and wisdom to cast off the old wounds of life while still preserving your spiritual and emotional values.

It was once the custom of many Cherokee parents to inflict some type of physical punishment upon their children when they misbehaved, but this was done in a way that was meant to teach a lesson as well as discipline the child. One of the most common methods involved the use of birch switches, which are flexible enough to make little impression on small behinds while still making a point. Seven switches were gathered in the forest and each was used just one time before it was broken in half and discarded. In this way parents were able to punish without inflicting any real physical pain, and the bad deed, like the seven broken switches, was discarded, never to be brought up again. It was much more a spirit representation of punishment done on all four levels with no anger involved.

The same very flexible branches have also been bundled up and affixed to a broom handle to use in house cleaning, just as we must periodically clean our spiritual 'houses'. Birch is the preferred material for witches' brooms as it symbolizes the process of cleaning out old dirt and dust from ourselves as well as our environment.

The wood of the birch tree is a powerful protector against the storms, both physical and emotional, that periodically enter our lives. It is often used to make healing wands and is said to bring us more clearly the wisdom of our elders, both alive and those in the spirit world. It is also used to protect against lightning strikes and for repelling negative energy coming from other people or forces.

The bark can be fashioned into containers in which may be stored sacred objects. As a writing surface, it is also ideal for spells, magic formulas or even New Year resolutions. If there is a personal flaw that you wish to deal with and discard, try writing it on a piece of birch bark and casting it into a fire where it will be turned to ash.

Meditating under a birch tree will certainly give you a feeling of tranquillity and acceptance of the way other people view the world and how you view and judge yourself.

Dogwood
(*Cornus*, many species)

There are dogwoods of every description growing in gardens throughout Australia and indeed the world, and they reflect the abundance of varieties growing endemically in our planet's temperate areas.

There are Korean, Chinese and Japanese dogwoods, and dogwoods growing from the Himalayas to Siberia and through much of Europe and North America.

These striking shrubs and small trees, although well known for their contribution to many landscape situations, also have a more obscure role in herbal medicine. For the Original People of the world, dogwood not only supplied a valuable source of medicine but also provided (and still does in many areas) a vital connection to things spiritual and of the physical world.

To the Native Americans who lived in the eastern third of the country, the eastern or flowering dogwood (*C. florida*) had a special significance that went beyond its many medical uses. For those who had the responsibility of organizing the planting schedule for the many crops that were grown, particularly beans, squash and corn (The Three Sisters), the flowering of the dogwoods was the sign that the time was right to begin planting.

PHYSICAL ASPECTS

Dogwoods have a wide range of size and appearance. One species is actually a ground cover perennial and, although most are shrubs or small trees, the mountain or pacific dogwood can grow to more than twenty meters. Most are deciduous, with a notable exception being *C. capitata*, the evergreen dogwood.

All species show their relationship to one another through the exquisite flowers made up of four petal-like bracts which range in color from white to deep red, followed in summer by small to medium fruits. Most species produce a lovely autumn display before losing their leaves to expose the exceptionally vibrant bark of pink, yellow or red, depending on variety.

Dogwoods grow in a wide variety of habitats, ranging from high mountain stream-sides to near-desert environments. The trick in cultivating this plant is to mimic as closely as possible its original growing conditions. I know this seems like a bit of an informational cop-out, but one could write a book solely on the subject of dogwoods and their care. The best overall advice is simply to observe the tree or shrub for any signs of drought or over-watering and adjust accordingly. Needless to say, dogwoods whose native habitat is beside streams will require abundant watering through the summer, whilst those from the very dry regions of California will require little if any hot weather watering. Most of the dogwoods appreciate a good layer of mulch to keep the roots cooler and dislike chemical fertilizers. With a couple of exceptions, all seem to tolerate a fair bit of shade, particularly the eastern or flowering dogwood.

MEDICINAL ASPECTS

Medicinally, the root bark from *C. florida*, a small yet dramatic flowering tree has traditionally provided reliable relief from fevers, diarrhea and dysentery. It was used as a general tonic and astringent, and in the treatment of typhus.

Even after the introduction of the 'miraculous' cinchona bark from Peru, known as quinine, the root bark of dogwood was still frequently preferred in the treatment of malaria.

The outer bark of the stems was also widely used in much the same way but was considered less potent, therefore it tended to be employed in less severe cases. Because of its milder nature, the stem bark was also decocted for the relief of indigestion and flatulent colic, as a poultice for wounds and menstrual backaches, and was said to be used in large doses to get rid of internal worms.

Every part of this tree seems to have a use. The extraordinary creamy white flowers, now available in red, pink and rose varieties, were made into a tonic for moon-time weakness and backache. A flower tea was also occasionally taken to 'fever out' a 'flu, with the desirable side effect of causing a desire to sleep, and is said by some to resemble the calming effect of chamomile flowers. I was taught to pound or chew the smaller twigs to use as a bush toothbrush, and I must say that it certainly freshened the teeth and gums, as well as providing relief from toothache.

There are many other species of dogwood growing throughout North America and Canada. The majority of them are shrubs or small trees and they all seem to be used in similar fashion, probably owing to the similar chemical constituents of the related species. The most interesting of these, from a spiritual point of view, would have to be the red-twig dogwood, *C. stolonifera*, also known as red willow.

The bark of this plant is used as a spiritual offering, occasionally scattered over an area as a blessing but more commonly smoked. I should say at this point that it isn't actually the thin red outer bark that is used but rather the soft greenish inner bark, which is gently scraped off with a knife and lightly roasted until dry. This is then smoked on its own or in combination with tobacco or other herbs.

To the Chinese medical practitioner the species *C. officinalis* is known as *Shan chu yu* and is considered one of the minor tonic herbs, particularly useful for urinary infections. It is interesting to note that, unlike the American dogwoods, this variety seems to retard perspiration but still seems to have the familiar astringent quality. It is often mixed with other herbs to produce a fine kidney and bladder tonic.

Throughout the Orient, wherever dogwoods grace the landscape, there are always medicinal uses for this elegant plant. One of the few evergreen dogwoods comes from the Himalayas and is employed for many purposes, including internal and external infections, as a stomatic and in the treatment of certain skin diseases.

Many species of dogwood produce an unusual fruit which, although not amongst the best-tasting fruit in the forest, is quite edible raw or cooked. I am told that the fruit of both the Cornelian cherry (*C. mas*) and the evergreen dogwood (*C. capitata*) are made into delicious jams and preserves. The only variety I have personally tried was from the mountain dogwood, *C. nuttallii*, which I can best describe as good survival food.

In case you are interested, the name 'dogwood' came not because it had such a nice bark (pun intended), but because a decoction of the bark was used by the early settlers of America to cure their dogs of mange.

SPIRITUAL ASPECTS

Few plants have had such a significant impact on my spiritual development as dogwoods, particularly the red-twig dogwood. Just the thought of this shrub takes me back to a time when life was far less complicated and much simpler, when I cared only about myself and did not know the meaning of giving or receiving, either of myself or my knowledge.

The spirit of the dogwood opened me up to the reality of self-love by showing me the love, beauty and perfection that is the world of nature, and how the divinity of our own being makes us all a part of those qualities. Dogwoods open up the fourth and fifth chakras, which allow us to feel universal and unconditional love for ourselves and all our relations.

The flowers of most species open before the leaves appear, representing how God's love for us surrounds us long before we can accept our own love for ourselves and others. The four petals (bracts) represent the four sacred directions and the part they play in the creation of our reality, the world that surrounds us all. They symbolize the four levels of our own existence – the physical, mental, emotional and spiritual bodies that make up our essence – and how we become balanced and centered when we can live rightly on all four levels.

Dogwoods appreciate music and particularly enjoy compositions in the key of E flat or any related key. They will respond with an immediate outpouring of love and understanding, and on occasion will grace us with a vision.

This is the gift that the dogwood has to offer us. It is the heralder of spring, the hope that blooms after the long, cold winter and prepares us for the summer of love.

The simplest and quickest method of reproducing most dogwoods is by taking cuttings. These may be taken as soon as the new season's growth has begun to harden, usually in late spring or early summer. These slips can be placed in a rooting medium and then put in a partly shaded position, or better yet in a propagating shed, for a few months, until roots begin to develop. The rooted cuttings are then placed into individual pots and grown under shelter until the following spring, when they may be transplanted out into the garden.

For spreading varieties of dogwood such as *C. stolonifera*, the plant may be divided in autumn or winter and replanted where it is to grow. Large dormant cuttings (hardwood) up to thirty centimeters long can be cut off the parent plant in late autumn or winter and placed directly in the ground where they are to grow.

Most dogwoods can be layered or even air-layered to produce a larger plant in less time.

Starting these plants from seed will yield many more plants but they may take at least seven years to bloom. If the seeds are taken off any of the new varieties of *C. florida*, these will most likely revert to the original white flower coloration.

The seed must first be separated from the fruit, which is best done over a sink using a strainer. The cleaned seed may then be sown about a centimeter deep in a punnet or a pot filled with a good seed-raising mix and kept in the refrigerator throughout the winter at about five degrees Celsius. This container is then brought outside to a protected spot in the garden where the seeds will germinate in about a month, providing the soil is kept moist.

Eucalyptus

(*Eucalyptus*, many species)

When I was a child growing up in Southern California we lived less than a block away from North Hollywood Park. Before the park was divided in half by a freeway it was an ideal playground, complete with soft, deep lawns for football and softball, a dry river bed which flooded every wet winter, and many different species of *Eucalyptus*. Several of these served as bases or goalposts for our games and stood as silent guardians of our childhood.

I had always assumed that the gum trees were native to California, since they grew not only in the park but almost everywhere else I had travelled within the state. When I moved up to Marin county, just north of San Francisco, to go to school, I was astounded to discover in my first horticulture class that eucalypts were in fact not indigenous to California. Indeed, they weren't even native to America, having their origin in some place called Gondwanaland, now known as Australia.

One story I heard was that gum seeds were originally brought over from Australia in the hope that they would provide a faster growing alternative to the native trees such as pine and oak, which were seriously depleted after the gold rush of 1849. Thousands of hectares were planted in an effort to fill the demand for tall, fast growing timber. Unfortunately the trees, when grown in the Californian soil and climatic conditions, developed into short, multi-trunked trees that were all but useless for making long timbers needed for the building of mines and the many towns that sprang up throughout the state. They did, however, succeed in spreading like weeds and often took over the natural habitats that existed before the gold rush.

I guess if you're going to keep 'weeds' in your backyard, they had better be good ones, and the Americans did pick a great one when they picked the eucalyptus. Now the rest of the world is finding out what the Aborigines knew for a hundred centuries: that this species of tree has the ability to heal an incredibly wide range of ailments, from coughs and colds right down to hemorrhoids.

PHYSICAL ASPECTS

Gum trees come in all shapes and sizes. To do them any descriptive justice would take up the rest of this book, so I am going to ask you to do some of the work here. The next time you see a eucalyptus tree – and I don't think that will take very long – I want you to stop and really look at the tree for a while, then begin to describe it to yourself in detail. Don't just look at it but really see it. If you can, pick up a  leaf, crush it and give it a good whiff. Much of the world never grew up with such an intoxicating smell from a tree and we here in Australia often take this spectacular flora for granted. Look at the color and texture of the trunk. Feel it with your hands and, if possible, give it a hug. Note the feeling you get when you come into physical contact with it. To test your intuition, see if you can get some type of energy feedback from the tree before you read the section dealing with the spiritual aspects of eucalypts.

Here again we are looking at a species that can be grown in a very wide range of conditions, so it is hard to generalize about where and how the trees grow best. There are species that can tolerate (and in fact prefer) damp, boggy soil while others would keel over dead at the mere suggestion of over-watering. I guess I could make a broad statement about how gum trees will adapt to many situations, but once again that doesn't give you much of a clue as to which species grow where.

I can say that most of the species mentioned, such as *Eucalyptus polybractea*, *E. globra*, *E. macrorhyncha* and my personal favorite,

E. citriodora, will all perform well in most conditions. If you want more information on which eucalypts will do better in your particular area, consult staff at your local nursery or a good book on the subject.

All species are started by seed.

MEDICINAL ASPECTS

Probably the most widely used resource yielded from the gum tree is the essential oil which is processed from the leaves and appropriately called eucalyptus oil. This oil has very effective antiseptic qualities due to its concentration of cineole. It is this agent that gives eucalyptus oil its powerful anti-microbial attributes. When added to steaming water the oil reaches deep into delicate nasal and lung membranes, killing many types of infectious organisms.

The blue Mallee gum, *E. polybractea*, is considered to be the richest source of cineole and is grown extensively in many parts of the world for its commercial value. The oil of many species of gum contains cineole and is therefore effective in the treatment of coughs, colds, asthma and bronchitis and as a decongestant. It is also applied in the mouth, to treat cases of gingivitis and other gum diseases. Additionally, it has become popular as a safe and organic cleaning solution.

The oil of at least one other species, *E. citriodora*, is said to be effective against golden staph bacteria, yet we hear that this organism is fast becoming a serious health threat to hospital patients. It is also used to treat athlete's foot, is added to perfumes and is applied to the skin or burned in candles to repel mosquitoes.

The bark from a number of eucalypts, but most notably that of the red stringybark, *E. macrorhyncha*, contains a substance called rutin which has the effect of strengthening blood vessels and capillaries, making it useful in treating chronic nosebleeds, varicose veins and some forms of hemophilia, and in alleviating hemorrhoids. Perhaps it should be required medication for those of us stuck sitting in front of a computer, writing for hours at a time. The bark of this tree also provided the material used in the construction of Aboriginal huts and was later copied by the early settlers in Australia.

The Tasmanian blue gum, *E. globulus*, has been widely planted around the world, not only for its medicinal value, but also due to the fact that it has the ability to soak up enormous quantities of water from the ground, thereby lowering the water table. It has been responsible for converting much low-lying swamp ground into productive farmland, with the added benefit of supplying the growing herbal trade with a valuable product. How is it that people overseas are capitalizing on products that were discovered and passed on freely to the colonists by the Aborigines, who were in turn treated so horrendously by those who received this precious gift?

Another valuable medicine is derived from several species of *Eucalyptus* but particularly from the gum-topped bloodwood, *E. dichromophloia*. This species exudes a sticky red gum that has been used by traditional Aborigines in curing a variety of skin complaints, including rashes, ringworm, venereal sores and minor skin irritations. It can also be added to water and taken as a general tonic, for bladder inflammations and as a gargle for sore throats. The high tannin content contributes to the effectiveness of this gum, which is commonly called kino. Small pieces of the sap can be placed into painful tooth cavities to relieve pain. Aborigines also soaked the flowers of this, and many other, species of gum to use in the treatment of coughs and colds.

Besides their use in healing, eucalyptus trees have provided our original inhabitants with food in many forms. Some types of eucalyptus bark were roasted and pounded into an edible 'flour', whilst the seeds were considered an adequate emergency food. Many Aborigines are still able to locate and dig up long sections of roots in arid areas of Australia to provide themselves with water. By cutting the long root into sections, removing the bark and pounding it into a pulp, enough water is extracted to get through the long, dry periods when no other source of water is available.

With beneficial plants such as gum trees it is easy to see how Australian Aborigines have been able to adapt and thrive in this country for over 100,000 years.

SPIRITUAL ASPECTS

What I have learned in the last few years about the spiritual aspects of gums has only served to reinforce what was taught to me by the grandmothers during my childhood years. They stood silently there in the park, watching our ball games and races, and we were for the most part consciously unaware of the energy they were imparting to us, but on a deeper level we were all being grounded or earthed by these sentinels of our One Mother.

When I was alone, which in my childhood was quite a bit of the time, I would often go down to the park and sit under one particular tree that marked the fifty metre line in our football games. The thick cushiony carpet of couch grass grew right up to the tree and afforded me a comfortable resting place for my skinny little butt, while the trunk made a perfectly fitting backrest. I would sit there for what seemed like hours and just watch the world go by. The sun would be only lightly filtered before it touched my face and there were times when I thought this must be how heaven was.

I now know how badly I needed that specific energy. I was the perennial dreamer as a young boy (some things never change) and was about as etheric as one can get in this world. What I needed more than anything was grounding, and that is exactly what this tree does. It is the ultimate grounding tool, and if this is the message that you got in the earlier exercise then you receive seven gold stars in your celestial tally book.

The Aborigines knew of the powerful grounding effect of this tree and actually devised many means by which to enhance its positive powers, which counteracted the tree's tendency to 'over-ground'. I have been told that many of the Dreamtime stories are designed as a means to lessen this effect and, until our society embraces ways to soften the influence of this tree over our everyday life, we will continue to be a country of grounded people.

Being grounded is not a bad thing as such, but when it is not balanced with an equal portion of the etheric it can create attitudes that lead to dysfunctional activities. We see generations of men living and dying in Australia without ever getting past the basics – working in very grounded vocations and spending vast amounts of time on drinking with mates at the pub, playing or watching sports, gambling, lusting over women and a whole array of ventures, all of which ground us.

I am not saying that these are bad things to do; only that to do these things in excess, and with no way to counter this type of energy with things that are not of the physical, is detrimental. You can best see this imbalance in our culture at parties, where, at times, all the men stay on one side of the room while the women stay on the other. Anyone who goes to the 'other side' is viewed with suspicion. This is due to the polarity that exists between men and women in Australia. Women, who are by their very nature more etheric beings, are less affected by this national grounding mechanism and are having a hard time coping with any additional grounding coming from men. This dilemma can be easily rectified in this country, simply by women becoming more earthy and men becoming more etheric.

The grounding effect of the wood of eucalypts is an ideal medium for women to work in. Making a staff or walking stick of this wood, whether it be a branch or a piece of four by two, will help balance out your aspects as long as you personally do the work of crafting and empowering the item. Beating two clapper sticks in rhythm regularly will also help, as long as they are made of eucalyptus wood. Almost any object made of this wood, when worked with over a period of time, will have the desired results.

For men it is a matter of softening our energy through the burning of leaves in a short ceremony that some cultures call smudging. This is a process whereby individual leaves or several leaves are bunched together and set alight, with the flame being blown out as soon as it begins to burn well and the resulting smoke from the remainder of the smoldering leaf used like water to be 'washed' over the body. This has the effect of dissipating any overload of grounding energy and in regular doses will help you to balance your yin and yang.

It is common to see an area of ground that is being prepared for dancing or ceremony swept with a leafy branch. This is not to clean up any rubbish that has accumulated but rather to balance and cleanse the area so that it is in harmony with the intent of the event to take place. It is the combination of wood and leaf that makes it so balancing. Next time you are planning a barbecue or party, try this technique throughout the area you intend to use and see if it doesn't work for you as well as it has worked for the Aborigines for some 100,000 years.

Eucalyptus wood works well for men as well as for women in strengthening ties that need to exist between your soul and your body. A small amulet made of this wood and worn around the neck will help you establish a better communication between you and your body.

Remember that the body is the vehicle that the soul uses to travel around this earthly plane and it is vitally important that you get to know it well. If you ignore it in any way, it will go away. We must learn to investigate, know and nourish the flesh, for every part of it is sacred. When you lean up against a gum tree think about your body and how it is so like the body of our Earthmother. It has its mountains, its valleys and a few wide-open spaces. We are both largely made up of water; eat, breathe and age. Although we don't like to dwell on it too much, we too have creatures walking on our skin and in our liquid. Occasionally we have to do something to get rid of an unhealthy infestation.

Eucalyptus oil is a good way to clear your mind of any mental, emotional or spiritual infestations you may have concerning your body. Anoint it with eucalyptus oil to honor it for the beautiful manner in which it was made. It is truly a temple and to allow yourself or anyone else to abuse it is sacrilege.

Eucalyptus oil will help wash away any shame you have towards your body or its functioning. It will bring you closer to your body and help you to breathe in the life force that sustains it. The oil may be rubbed on the body or inhaled through an oil burner or vaporizer, or the leaves may simply be rubbed on your skin. Leaves placed inside a medicine bag will help to consolidate your physical experience and aid in your body awareness. They will also protect you from any negative physical denigration or abuse.

The seed capsules can be drilled, strung and worn around the wrist, ankle or neck. This will aid you when you are in need of a little grounding. Let the fragrance make you more aware of your breathing and allow you to breathe in the life force fully and more effectively.

Linden

(Tilia americana, T. cordata T. euchlora, T. tomentosa, T. x vulgaris)

There are certain plants that possess some indefinable energy which, at different times and places in my life, has drawn me close to them even when I was totally unaware of their power and the effect they were having on me. Many herbs undoubtedly have the ability to sense when we are in need and will come to our aid.

Early in my career I was involved mainly in the nursery and landscaping trade. During this time I found myself irresistibly drawn to plants that, while not unattractive in their own way, had some unknown quality to them that set them apart from the rest. As I became more fascinated with herbs and herbal lore I discovered that most, if not all, of these plants had medicinal or spiritual attributes that somehow related to particular health or emotional issues confronting me at the time. I'm now sure that this is the reason that the linden tree has only in the last four years come so surely and dominantly into my awareness.

Before this current period of my life I was fortunate to have very little stress or emotional upheaval confronting me. Now, as for many of us, it seems that things have become a lot harder. Maybe it's just a fact of life that, due to things like having children, suffering the trauma and heartbreak of separation and divorce, experiencing a mid-life crisis, living in financial poverty with the loss of a job, or simply having to meet a publisher's deadline, we begin to find ourselves barely able to hold our heads above the emotional high tide.

It is times like this when plants like the linden come calling at our doorstep to bring us a semblance of peace and calm in the storm. Now, hardly a day goes by when the gentle voice of the basswood (the American name for *Tilia*) does not enter my reality. Whether as an illustration in a book or growing in the park or at a friend's house, she continues to present herself to me in a way I can no longer ignore, for linden trees are all about finding peace, tranquillity and the centre of the universe again.

PHYSICAL ASPECTS

The linden tree is often detected by smell in summer rather than its inconspicuous form or shape. It tends to be a slow to moderate grower that can live to be a thousand years old and will achieve a height of some ten to twenty meters. It has a dense, pyramidal shape, and oval or heart-shaped leaves.

Its true glory comes in early summer, after many other trees have finished their blooming. Very fragrant flowers emerge as small, drooping, bleached yellow flowers which often literally drip with nectar, to the delight of bees and honeyeaters. Take time to look at the remarkable apparatus that supports the flowers and will later disperse the seed. One can easily see how Leonardo Da Vinci got his idea for some of the flying devices he drew. The pendulous clusters of seed are attached to a modified leaf structure shaped a bit like a cross between a surfboard and a hang glider. The bark is usually grey and lightly furrowed. It is often difficult to tell species apart as they tend to cross-breed readily.

Linden loves rich, deep soils but will tolerate average garden soil, particularly if it is well mulched. These trees prefer full sun and an occasional deep soaking, although they can be fairly drought resistant when well established.

Young trees do tend to be a little floppy at first so it might be advisable to stake them loosely. While we're on the subject it might be a good time for a little lesson (and this might apply to raising children as well as trees). Horticultural science, after much testing, discovered that a tree that has been securely tied to a stake with room to grow but not to move freely will develop a much weaker trunk than one that has been allowed to sway about, for it is the moving back and forth that strengthens the wood. When attaching a tree to a stake make sure to allow it room to move with the wind.

Linden trees are propagated by seed sown in autumn. Make sure the soil stays moist but not soggy. Cuttings can also be taken in summer.

MEDICINAL ASPECTS

On both sides of the Atlantic we find that the Original People knew all about the healing qualities of this genus of trees.

The dangling flowers have been considered the ideal medicine for a wide variety of ailments but most importantly as a treatment for nervous conditions and their manifestations. Being in an anxious state often brings on a variety of symptoms. For me it starts as an inability to eat at the appropriate times, particularly at breakfast. I often feel nauseous and, if the stress is extreme, I will literally be sick to my stomach. This is often followed by sleeplessness, a restless feeling, anxiety and rising blood pressure. Fortunately these symptoms always occur soon after that first day in late summer when suddenly the sun moves into autumn mode. This condition, common in many people, has been named by the medical establishment 'seasonal affective disorder', or SAD. I say fortunately because, by this time of the year, nature has already rewarded me for a summer of hard work by supplying me with many great herbs for just such a condition. Thanks to skullcap, St John's wort and Ashwaganda, I find that before long I am working through my stress, but it is linden that puts my stomach back where it belongs.

Besides being of benefit to nervous conditions, linden has a long history of medical applications. In Europe the flowers, and to a lesser extent the leaves, were utilized extensively for high blood pressure, vomiting, insomnia, relaxation of the nervous system, hysteria and headache. Linden flowers also found favor as a tonic and in clearing phlegm or excess mucus from the throat and lungs. The fruit was made into jelly, not only for its superb taste but also as a remedy for hangovers, particularly when the stomach and pancreas were affected.

Like their European 'relatives', many Native American people inhabiting the eastern third of North America and Canada found it useful for similar conditions, although they tended to use it much more sparingly internally. The reasons for this might be twofold. First, I believe that the lives of Native Americans were far less stressful than those of their European counterparts; and second, they seem to have found that the American linden made them nauseous. This is to do with the fact that the American linden contains an ingredient not found in the European linden.

They did, however, find many other uses for what they called basswood. Although still utilized internally for similar complaints, this was the simmered bark that served as a cure for boils, eczema and other skin rashes, sores and inflamed wounds. It was placed, fresh, immediately on burns. The Cherokee would boil down the bark and, when it became a sticky mess, mix it with cornmeal for drawing out pus from a particularly nasty boil or carbuncle. It was also believed that chewing a piece of bark from a lightning-struck tree and applying it externally would cure a rattlesnake bite.

The most common Indian use of basswood was, however, in the manufacturing of string, rope and thread. For this purpose the bark would be simmered for a time until it became soft and pliable and then pounded until it became fibrous. Virtually every household would have a variety of strings, wound into balls and used when needed for making fishing line and nets, binding timber together, building or repairing furniture, constructing snowshoes and anything else that you can fix with string.

It is a little-known fact that many Indian tribes were proficient in surgical techniques of many types using obsidian flakes for scalpels that were sharper than our modern steel scalpels, and basswood fibers for thread. How ironic it is that, after hundreds of years practicing surgery in our present society, we still have a higher incidence of post-operative infections than our Indian counterparts did, and no one ever received a bill for the healing.

SPIRITUAL ASPECTS

Imagine stepping into a world where soft music is heard in the wind, where peace and tranquillity are found under a cool shade tree on a warm summer day. The air is filled with the droning of bees trying their best to fly upside-down holding onto a flower while gulping fragrant nectar. The intoxicating smell rekindles some ancient genetic memory that you can't quite identify. You can feel the timelessness of childhood and the serenity of old age when you have lived well. These intangible things can be yours if you will only take the moment and relax under the linden tree.

It is said that unruly children begin to quieten down once they are seated under the spreading canopy of this loving, calm, protective tree. The leaves, if carried in one's pocket, will increase our projection of love for others. The hard seeds work to energize the solar plexus if placed in a medicine bag and worn above this spot. Depression in many cases is a result of a slowdown in the energy that gets distributed by the solar plexus and the seeds will help to stabilize the flow.

Many people from original cultures throughout the world made masks from the wood of the linden tree. This wood is soft and free of splinters but more importantly it represents the mask that we hold in front of our souls, the ego. By working with the wood we can form shapes, figures or masks that represent our egos to be able to see them better. *Pahos*, or prayer sticks, can be fashioned as well. They are not idols, but rather objects of prayer that symbolize the physical manifestation of a spiritual activity. *Pahos* are usually carved and decorated with paint, cloth, feathers, or whatever reminds you of what you are praying for, and once they are inserted into the ground and the prayer is delivered, they are left to the elements, never to be used again. Make it a good prayer. Lucky charms are also good to carve out of this soft wood.

The early Germanic people who inhabited Europe long ago considered linden to be sacred. The more I learn about this culture, the more I believe that they must have had contact with their Native American brothers long before the Vikings or Christopher Columbus. I'll talk more about that later in the book.

Plants of the *Tilia* genus have a strong protective quality and, if a staff of their wood is hung over the door of your house, will guard against any negative forces that try to enter it.

Lastly, I will leave you with this bit of lore. It is said that, if your baby is slow to start walking, gather up a large handful of linden twigs, place them in roughly twelve liters of water and boil until two-thirds of the water has evaporated. After the water cools, pour the contents of the pot over the baby's legs twice a day until the child begins to walk.

Peach, plum and cherry
(*Prunus*, many species)

We rarely think, as we push our shopping trolleys through the produce department of the local supermarket, about the fact that we are, in many ways, looking at numerous herbs disguised as fruits and vegetables. Most members of the Cole family, such as broccoli and cabbage, are marvellous for cleaning out toxins from the lower tract and protecting us from cancer. Asparagus acts as a kidney cleanser and a mild diuretic, while cooked tomatoes are now said to be good for correcting high blood pressure. Would you be surprised, then, if I told you that for centuries the humble peach, plum and wild cherry trees have been used not just for food, but also for an amazing array of medical and spiritual purposes?

If we look more closely at the whole genus of *Prunus*, which includes peaches, nectarines, cherries, plums, almonds, prunes, apricots and many others, we can see how valuable it is in the kitchen. Only when we see past the tip of this fruit-bowl iceberg do we begin to appreciate the valuable contribution to our health and well-being that the rest of the tree has offered. I will try to condense into a few pages a story that will take us to four continents and many nations.

In North America the primary representative of this genus was, before the coming of the white settlers, the wild cherry or chokecherry. The three main species were *Prunus virginiana*, *P. demissa* and *P. serotina*.

PHYSICAL ASPECTS
Almost all of the medicinal and edible *Prunus* trees are deciduous, losing their leaves in a very colorful way and adding a pleasant variety of hues to autumn's already spectacular exhibition. Although occasionally used medicinally, all evergreen varieties should be considered very poisonous. When in doubt, don't.

Most grow to about seven or eight meters, although it is best to keep them relatively small through pruning and this will also make

them fruit better if done correctly. All varieties bear lovely white to pink flowers in spring, usually before the foliage emerges. It is often the first good feed the bees have had in a long time and if you are lucky they will get to work to set your summer fruit. The wild species of cherry and plum can be scrubby looking and not nearly as symmetrically balanced as the domesti-
cated varieties. They nonetheless have a beauty all their own.

All have extraordinary bark that ranges in color from greyish-pink to deep, almost black, red. Look long and closely some day to this sometimes hidden treasure and you will see a lot more than you bargained for.

Most species of *Prunus* prefer rich, well drained soils and are best grown in the full sun. To be at their best they all prefer a good feed and deep watering during the summer months, but still seem to perform when neglected. Some, like the peach, are susceptible to bacterial and fungal problems, so keep an eye out. There are organic alternatives to these problems but chemical sprays seem to dominate the approach to the ailments. Most of the native species are pretty tolerant of conditions and are very drought resistant. Peach is the most demanding if you want decent fruit. They require regular winter pruning and plenty of water to achieve maximum fruiting.

All 'wild' species are started from seed or cuttings taken during the summer. All domestic fruit varieties are best bought at your local nursery.

MEDICINAL ASPECTS

If you've ever tasted a wild cherry without any preparation you would know why it is also called a chokecherry. I've heard that the taste is more palatable after a good frost but when I had my first experience with eating the raw fruit I decided to make it my last. Although the fruit was consumed in vast quantities by most Indians, it was most often dried, ground up or buried in the earth for a few weeks to make it edible. It was also mixed with meat and fat to make pemmican, a nutritious food of chewable consistency that could be stored throughout the year for consumption when fruit was out of season. It was, however, the bark and root bark that provided (and still do) a superb medicine used for dozens of ailments and conditions.

My ancestors, both Cherokee and Pennsylvanian German, used the bark of *P. serotina* to treat fevers, colds and particularly coughs. Mixed with dogwood and corn whisky, it was employed for measles. A warm tea of the bark was administered to women exhibiting the first signs of labor pains. The Catawba people also used it for expectant mothers, in a mixture that combined dogwood and poplar bark. When mixed with horsemint (*Monarda mollis*) it could be employed internally to get rid of intestinal worms.

Probably the most interesting use of the dried and ground bark of this invaluable gift from the heavens, and another that dispels the notion that Amerindians were largely an uncivilized bunch of heathens with little or no medical skill or knowledge, is as an antiseptic, steric (blood clotter) and pain reliever for the stumps of amputated limbs. In areas where the extreme cold of winter was often responsible for frostbite and gangrenous extremities, surgery could be crucial in the fight to save lives. Amputation or the surgical removal of dead, gangrenous tissue was a well-known procedure many thousands of years ago in North America, Canada and, indeed, many other regions of the 'primitive' world.

Another invention that the Native American culture gave compassionately and freely to the early European settlers was a good-tasting cough syrup made from the bark of the chokecherry, which was to become the mainstay of American cough remedies for the next two hundred years. The flavoring is still used today in many medicines. The species *P. serotina* is used in modern natural medicines to control stubborn coughs and bronchitis, to coax sluggish appetites and for its anti-viral and anti-bacterial properties.

As we move across the Atlantic to Africa we find the bark of the native species of the region (*P. africana*) being employed as a very effective treatment against enlarged prostate glands. So impressive are its effects that it is now being used worldwide, and this has led to serious over-exploitation of the natural stands of this tree. Vast plantations are now being established to preserve the remaining native stands.

The plum (*P. domestica*) is said to have been cultivated longer than any other fruit, with the exception of the apple. It has been used as food and medicine since prehistoric times and has a host of legends and folk tales attached to it. The plum that we have all come to know and love originally came from Eurasia but its use spread quickly throughout the rest of temperate Europe and Asia to supplant other less exotic wild plums. Ironically plums are now classified as either a European or a Japanese variety, even though they are most likely to have originated in Persia. This is due to the fact that, wherever the plum from Persia went, whether it was Europe, Asia or much later to America, it was cross-pollinated and improved with the local variety. Now we have literally hundreds of varieties spanning several different species, but they all still seem to hold at least some of their original healing powers.

We probably know the plum and her relative, the prune, for its laxative action which, as the commercials say, is gentle and effective. These fruits have also been used to stimulate appetite and improve digestion. The bark of the plum tree was ironically employed in the treatment of diarrhea as well as a tonic for the kidney and bladder. It was also said to settle the stomach and ease vomiting through its mild sedative quality. The bark and root bark have been found to contain a substance called phloretin which is said to be effective against gram positive and negative bacteria. In North America and Canada the native species, *P. americana*, found almost identical use.

Once again we see how the knowledge of healing throughout the world has been brought together for the benefit of all. All of our ancestors, whether they be from Asia, Europe, Africa, North and South America or Australia, call out to us at this time to share our knowledge and lives so that we may all live on this Earth as one.

SPIRITUAL ASPECTS

There can be no story that better tells of the deep spiritual connection between humans and trees than the tale of Chief Joseph who, in the latter part of the 1800s, led the Nez Perce people living in what are now parts of Idaho and Montana.

He was a brave and loving man who wanted nothing more for his people than peace and freedom. Time and time again the government tried to force him and his people to the reservation, until he felt he had no option. Once there they were not given the food, shelter and clothing they had been promised by the government, so many, including Chief Joseph, fled. He made every attempt to avoid war but it was only when he heard that his prized peach orchard had been destroyed by the cavalry that he finally took up arms. It was more than just a fruit orchard to him. It represented the tree of life, the wood that was skillfully formed into the pipestems to which he attached the sacred pipe and inhaled the will and dreams of the Creator, and it was from the branches that he fashioned prayer sticks, attaching tobacco ties and offering them as prayers for the sick. He had spent many summers savoring the ripe fruit and sharing it with his relations, the bears and birds, and now they were destroyed. It is a story I recall when I think I've got troubles and it always makes me realize that I have no real problems.

All prunus trees possess the ability to connect our spiritual activities to the material world for without this balance many who seek the truths of life end up 'lost in space'. It is important that every spiritual concept is in some way brought into the physical plane, as was done in all indigenous cultures. That is why art and craft work has always been part and parcel of every spiritually aware culture. Things seen in visioning or dreaming become cemented or manifested in the material world only when they are 'reconstructed' by fashioning spiritual or artistic items that represent the etheric world.

The wood from all prunus is special and contains many divine characteristics. It represents love and how it is best served through a connection between the worlds. A finished staff or pipestem is breathtaking to touch and feel. It can act as a bridge between the physical and spiritual worlds and brings through and amplifies the healing energy from Spirit. It is a channel through which travels God's own healing power. When used in healing, such wood can double or triple your ability to pass this power through you. Placed over your door it can ward off any foolish spells or magic projected by others.

The cherry is also very powerful and is often stripped of its bark and made into prayer sticks, known by the Dakota Sioux as *Wau ya pi*, and sacred hoops which represent the spiritual circle that we are all a part of. The prayer stick is usually carved, painted and decorated with feathers and bits of cloth, and a bundle containing some type of offering (usually tobacco) attached to the top. The prayer sticks are left outside or on an altar and offered as a prayer for someone sick.

The American black cherry is of particular significance to those who participate in the Sun Dance as it is always held on the first day of the full moon after the black cherries are ripe. This day is known in the Sioux language as *Ca Pa-sapa-wi* – literally, the black cherry moon.

In much of China peach tree branches are used to chase away evil spirits and it is said that you will live longer if you carry a piece of the wood in your pocket or medicine pouch. There is, in fact, a worldwide belief in the divining and magical powers that inhabit these trees.

Spheres made from peach wood have a tendency to move when

there is a spirit present or close by. They will vibrate if the influence is a negative one and roll smoothly if it is of good nature. The wood can also be used like crystal balls to foretell future events.

From caring for, or even just sitting under, one of these trees, you will be able to feel the energy of the Earth rising up the trunk and meeting with the sun's life-giving strength to fill each branch with the dance of life. From its limbs we learn about what love really is: it is never born out of want or desire but only ever comes through unconditional love for oneself and all other life; it is the act of unconditional giving and sharing of self and property. Eating a fully ripe, sweet fruit is a most sensual experience and will help to open up your heart chakra. Sharing one is even better.

Poplar
(*Populus*, many species)

If you are one of those people who studied Latin you would probably know that the name for this tree comes to us from the Roman term *arbor populi*, which means 'tree of the people'. Of course it wouldn't take a Latin major to figure this one out, for anyone who recognizes this very common tree would know just how popular it is, hence the name. In Roman times most city streets and parks or common areas were planted in poplar due to their fast growing habit, their cooling shade and for the mellowing energy they radiate.

Popular though this green oasis is, few people would know that it is a veritable cornucopia of medical and food value, and in its natural environment it is a generous host to hundreds of other life forms providing food, lodging and health to all those who seek it.

The most obvious example is in North America. Here the beaver has embraced a symbiotic relationship with the poplar or aspen tree by utilizing the wood to build its home, which it lines with great quantities of branches to eat during the winter. The beaver, in turn, helps the aspen by building its 'dam house' in spots along the river that are prone to occasional flooding. Through their building activities, the beavers flood larger areas, thereby killing off neighboring pine stands and creating new, ideal conditions for the aspen to thrive in.

The poplar/aspen provides a life-saving refuge for many species of animal such as moose, deer and elk during the harsh winter months when grasses are hard to obtain. It is not unusual to see groves of poplar trees, the lower branches of which have been stripped of their nutritious bark by hungry mammals in times of need. We human animals, being no exception and being so inventive, have found hundreds of other uses for this beneficent tree species.

Many Native American people gathered quantities of branches during the winter to supply their horses with forage when the grasses were covered with snow. The bark also supplied them with the tinder necessary to roast the clay that was used in body painting and ceremonial paintings.

The wood played a vital role in the everyday life of Native Americans as well as in their most holy spiritual practices. Being lightweight and pliable it was fashioned into saddle bases, lances, cradle boards and items of furniture. Fully mature catkins were a source for the yellow dye that was used to color arrow plumes. The wood is also one of the best to use in getting a fire started and provides a cool but bright fire in the summer.

The Navajo still play a game called *Da'aka'tsosts'id*, a version of two-up, in which six rectangular pieces of poplar wood are painted white on one side and black on the other, with a seventh painted white and red (this is the wild card). These 'dice' are tossed in the air and the points are awarded according to how many land white side up.

Adults were not the only ones to utilize poplar in games. For the children of the plains-dwelling Amerindians the wood was used to carve dolls and representations of horses, buffalo and other wild animals. A common activity among young girls was to make miniature tipi camps out of the heart-shaped leaves found on the cottonwood tree (*P. fremontii*) or aspen (*P. tremuloides*) and to play 'house' (or, more appropriately, 'village') in them. Also a favorite pastime among Indian children was to chew the gum made from the emerging flower catkins.

PHYSICAL ASPECTS

All poplars are known as fast grow-ing deciduous trees, often exceeding three meters of growth in one sea-son. Most species reach a maximum height of about twenty meters, although the aspen usually stays much smaller. Many produce suck-ering roots, which increase their numbers. This can be a good thing  if you wish your poplar stand to spread rapidly but a bad thing if you plant it carelessly. The majority of trees in this species are relatively short-lived, although they make up for it by their prolific suckering. Old ones die but new ones grow quickly to take their place.

Most species have beautifully furrowed bark that is white, grey and black. An exception is the aspen, which has quite striking smooth white bark contrasting with the light green oval leaves.

Most species have glossy, heart-shaped leaves that move even when there is scarcely a breeze. The white poplar, *P. alba*, has con-trasting leaves – dark on the top and white underneath – giving the tree the appearance of an organic strobe lightshow in a good wind.

Long, willow-like catkins are produced in abundant tassels in spring and are followed by downy seeds which fill the air in the slightest breeze.

Most species prefer areas that keep moist in the summer months, although they all have the ability to tap into any water source such as an underground creek or aquifer. For this reason they are at their best if planted in areas where the water table needs lowering and if kept away from houses, sewer lines or tanks, water pipes or wherever the suckers can do damage, such as in driveways or footpaths.

This is a tree for the wide open spaces, not for a normal house block. Although they will grow in all but the tropical areas, they are at their best in temperate climates with warm summers and cool winters. They all benefit from occasional deep waterings in the heat of summer.

All poplars can be propagated by taking root or stem cuttings in late summer to early winter. These can be quite large and they require no special preparation.

MEDICINAL ASPECTS

Besides being eaten as a highly nutritive food, the bark of the poplar, which I must admit is rather too bitter for everyday consumption, has enjoyed a well deserved reputation as an effective treatment for stomach trouble, including poor appetite and diarrhea, when boiled into a tea. It is perhaps more commonly used in combination with other herbs, such as black cohosh and goldenseal, as a stimulant to sluggish appetites and to increase the function of the liver and urinary tract. It is also said to be good for sore throats and laryngitis, used as a gargle, and for hemorrhoids. In several recent studies the bark of young shoots from *P. tacamahaca* (which, by the way, tends to be far sweeter and less bitter than the bark from older trees) has been found to be effective against the bacteria responsible for tuberculosis.

The dormant winter buds of the poplar are called Balm of Gilead. However, this term can be a very misleading and confusing term when used in herbal medicine. It has its origins in early biblical writings, when it was used to refer to an evergreen tree originating in Africa and Asia Minor called *Commiphora opobalsamum*. A fragrant resin was obtained from this tree which was used extensively in medicine as well as spiritually. Nowadays the name usually refers to the aromatic winter buds that are gathered from a number of different species of *Populus*, but most commonly *Populus* x *candicans*, also called *P. balsamifera, P. gileadensis* and *P. nigra*. To make things even more complicated, there is yet another plant that is referred to as Balm of Gilead – *Cedronell canariensis* – which only *smells* like the real thing and has no relationship to any of the aforementioned species. For the sake of convenience and sanity I will use the name only in referring to the dormant leaf buds of several species of poplar.

The winter buds have been used on both sides of the Atlantic for a wide variety of purposes. Most common is the practice of boiling these buds in vegetable or animal fats and applying the resulting mixture externally to areas of the body that are affected by arthritis, rheumatism, swollen and inflamed joints, burns, bruising and cuts. This mixture was also applied to the forehead and cheeks to alleviate headaches and was rubbed on the chest and into nasal passages to relieve congestion and 'flu symptoms. The Potwatomis of the Great Lakes area tended to use it more for problems such as eczema and skin irritations.

At one time there was a popular ointment, sold at every chemist or apothecary, called *Unguentum populeon*. This derivative of the resins of poplar buds and leaves was said to be a panacea for almost every illness known to human or beast, and many modern salves and ointments used to relieve the manifestations of colds and 'flu contain the same resins. Since the active constituents in the buds are not soluble in water they are most commonly extracted for use in a good quality oil such as olive or almond if you are making an ointment for external use, or in alcohol if you wish to make a tincture.

Just so that no part of the poplar goes unnoticed I will mention that the root was used by the Chippewa as a preventative against premature births and that the Delaware used the same decoction as a tonic for general weakness.

SPIRITUAL ASPECTS

All poplars, but particularly the quaking aspen, possess the ability to speak to us in any language and at any time. If you feel lost for an answer about life's many questions, seek out the aspen tree, for she will always speak the truth. She helps us look deeply inward and to the Great Beyond in our quest for self-enlightenment and the purpose for our existence. When the wind is so quiet that you cannot hear it speak or feel it touch your inner self, the aspen will tremble the wind's voice, amplifying it so that our ears may hear and our hearts understand. This is why the Creator made the aspen the only broadleaved tree growing from coast to coast in America: so that her people, the Native Americans could always hear her will. The wind has not ceased in its holy communication with us; rather, we have lost the time needed to hear. The aspen will help facilitate this communion through her ability to speed the message through in this time when we seem to have no time.

The heart-shaped leaves of the poplar show us that love is everywhere. There are few forces in the world that have greater love for humankind than trees, and this is the truth that is displayed in her flashing foliage.

She is the personification of all five elements of this world: Earth, as signified by her deep connection with our Earthmother; wind, as signified by her ability to represent the wind on the earthly plane; water, as her lifeblood being drawn out of the depths of the earth and expelled through her pores in a luxurious stomatic display of extravagance (even in the heat of the summer, when most other trees have slowed down their metabolism to near standstill, her heart still beats strongly and soundly); fire, as represented in the sacred fire that is built with her wood, a light that will kindle brightly but will not burn; and finally, love, the fifth element, which is all around us and which we seek in everything we do, yet which eludes us when we need it the most. Work, family, religion, sex, money and fame are all ways in which we seek the love and approval of others, often without much success. It is the deeper Love – capital L – that we must learn to embrace and it only ever comes from within. We find it only when we give ourselves permission to be loved as imperfect beings in an imperfect world. God loves us always and forever – this we know; but we must also know that it is often necessary to hear this for ourselves, and for that we need only the time to sit in the aspen grove for a spell.

If you wish to attract financial abundance in your life, try putting a few poplar leaves in your wallet, and place the wallet in a cloth bag with a strap that can be slung over the shoulder so that the bag fits a close but comfortable distance under your armpit. This will also help protect you against bankruptcy and pickpockets.

If you wish to find love, do not place the leaves in your wallet, especially if you keep your wallet in your back pocket, or the person who comes into your life will be a 'pain in the butt' and will only love you for your money. You can imagine what sort of person you would attract if you were to put a few leaves in your underwear!

Try putting a few leaves in a medicine pouch or bag that is worn around the neck, but not too close to your neck or you will attract a pain in the neck. Just make sure it is worn over your heart and everything should be okay.

I know a few witches, good ones of course, who add a bit of poplar ointment to their flying potions to help them ease more gracefully out of their physical bodies when astral projecting.

Many Amerindians consider the wood of the poplar sacred; it can be used to carve objects with spiritual significance. The roots, which hold the greatest energy, must be collected only in the winter and be dried slowly but thoroughly until well cured; otherwise the wood will split and be useless. The shavings may be placed in a medicine bag to ensure abundance.

Willow
(*Salix*, many species)

The wood from this plant, being extremely pliable when wet or green, has many utilitarian uses. We are probably all familiar with wicker furniture, which comes from this plant, and are at least aware of the use of willow in making a wide variety of crafted objects such as fish and animal traps, nets, bows, bags, and as a framework for sweat lodges (saunas), houses and many furnishings, as well as for snowshoes and most importantly for making baskets. In many cultures, certain surgical instruments such as forceps to remove arrowheads or any other embedded foreign objects were fashioned out of willow wood. Last but certainly not least, cricket bats made from willow wood are said to give a mighty wallop.

The seed 'fluff' is still used occasionally in spinning.

PHYSICAL ASPECTS

Willows range dramatically in size and shape. Some species, such as the European or common willow, grow to about twenty-five meters, with an almost equal spread. One American species, *Salix nigra*, although narrower, will often reach this height as well although the majority of species stay at  about ten to twenty meters. The leaves of most willows are long and narrow, with at least some serrations along the leaf margin. Many produce lovely yellowish catkins or flowers early in spring, often before the foliage emerges. The flowers of the pussy willow, S. *discolor*, sprout in winter and make a good addition to cut flower arrangements when there is little else blooming. The leaves are usually a pale but attractive green whilst the bark is generally quite dark, sometimes black. Probably the best known species is the weeping willow, *S. babylonica*, which has a soft yet dramatic form with, as its name implies, a pronounced weeping growth habit, making it an ideal feature tree.

The willow is synonymous with water and is best grown near or around it. All trees are extremely fast growers and require plenty of room and moist to wet soil, although a few species are more tolerant to drought. All will begin to defoliate if left dry for any length of time, but recover quickly. Most will perform best in full sun but should be kept well away from any drainage pipes as the roots tend to be very aggressive. It is generally very difficult to plant anything under these trees.

MEDICINAL ASPECTS

The next time you have one of those headaches that meditation, relaxation or visualization just won't cure and it's time to take a couple of aspirin, give a few moments of thanks to the plant that made it all possible, the willow. The chemical responsible for alleviating our headaches, pains and discomfort is called acetylsalicylic acid and it has become one of the most commonly taken legal drugs in the world.

It was known for eons that the bark of many species of willow had the ability to alleviate painful ailments such as headaches, sore throats and elevated body temperature and ease the discomfort and inflammation in certain forms of arthritis and rheumatism. It was not until the mid-1800s that aspirin was synthesized from a derivative of willow bark, salicin or salicylic acid.

Aspirin has to be ranked as one of the marvellous inventions that our technological brains have devised, but its success is also an indictment on our society, for it is doubtful that there has been any society in history that has needed to use such quantities of medication for headaches. This is the most common symptom of the effect that our lifestyle has on us, stress being the commonest cause of the headache pandemic. We now live in a world that is suffering what many indigenous cultures call 'the disease of civilization'. As we tighten muscles, constrict our blood vessels and restrict the flow of blood to our brains, we get a message to relax and deal with the issues that have caused our head to feel like it is literally going to split. It is often not acceptable to do this, due to the demands that we place on ourselves and is much easier in the short term to take a couple of painkillers to mask the symptoms of this stress. We spend billions of dollars each year to basically hide the symptomology of the disease of civilization.

Before the world became like it is today, everyone had the time and support of their society to treat what was then a relatively rare condition – and it was usually treated with willow bark, along with a healthy dose of tender loving care such as massage, guided meditation, curative music, acupressure or the application of healing hands.

More often the bark from the willow tree or shrub was utilized to lower fevers and reduce connective tissue inflammation. In North America and Canada, where willows are common from coast to coast, it was employed as a contraceptive or a dressing for infected or gangrenous wounds and to stop bleeding. It was also added to foot baths to cool down sweaty feet and as a deodorizer. The Pensobscots, who dwelled in what is now the state of Maine, often smoked the bark to treat asthma and also made a mush-like substance which was applied to the forehead in the treatment of headaches.

Juice pressed from the bark was dripped into the nostrils to relieve fevers and into the eyes to soothe them. In stronger doses, willow bark was considered an excellent purgative and is still used for this purpose today, particularly in preparation for the Sun Dance. The powdered bark was occasionally used to stimulate lactation. The native people of North America and Canada still use a decoction of the inner bark to treat deep wounds and sore throats.

In Europe we find many of the same uses for this wonderful species of plant. As well as a common antiseptic, the inner bark and leaves of the common willow, *S. alba*, were also used to treat dysentery, insomnia and certain digestive disorders. By the time Maud Grieve wrote her famous 1930s book on herbs, the willow was being credited with curing 'nocturnal emissions', gonorrhea and ovarian pain, and as an aphrodisiac. I cannot, however, personally vouch for the effectiveness of any of these treatments.

Interesting to note here is that the early pilgrim settlers to America thought the buds of the willow to be an anti-aphrodisiac. It might be that they needed as many herbal tools to combat lustful feelings as they could find, given the repressed sexual nature of the culture at the time. Again, I have no personal experience with this use.

SPIRITUAL ASPECTS

Native people living in the eastern third of what is now the United States, including the 'five civilized tribes', the Creek, Cherokee, Seminole, Choctaw and the Chicasaw, all once performed a ceremony called the Green Corn ceremony, held each year in autumn to celebrate the ripening of the corn in the many fields that were cultivated by these tribes.

Beans, corn and squash, collectively known as The Three Sisters, played a vital role in feeding these people, but corn represented, as it still does today, our connection with our Earthmother and the world of Spirit. To many people it is a physical manifestation of the Old Corn Woman (or Corn Maiden, as she is known in some regions). It was she who brought corn to the Principal People and imparted it with her life-giving breath, she who taught the people how to prepare it and she who gave us a new way of life.

The dancing, singing and ceremonies often lasted for up to seven days, but before anything got started each person involved with the festival was required to participate in a cleansing ceremony which involved ritually bathing in and drinking a quantity of a cool decoction containing the pounded roots of the pussy willow, S. humilis. Each person would then go off and regurgitate the liquid. This would be done to purify, inside and out, each participant and bring in the medicine, or energy necessary to appease the Above Beings.

The Green Corn ceremony also marked the time of the year when the vitality of summer is replaced by the autumnal pulling in of the life forces, and this is what the willow represents: this energy, pulled into the bark of the willow during autumn and released in spring, when the bark is harvested and made into medicines.

For us, willow symbolizes the unblocking of emotions in an effort to feel the pain on the spiritual level rather than on the physical level. It is through our experience of emotional pain that we gain a clearer picture of what it is that needs to be cleared up. When emotion is repressed it is often experienced through a headache, literally manifesting that repressed pain as physical pain. When we take aspirin we can block the physical pain but it still exists on the etheric plane and can come back time and time again.

When we work with the essence of the willow we can tap into emotional issues that have been buried for some time. This often leads to a profound but healing confrontation with things woven into our society that give us enigmatic feelings of desertion, grief and desolation. We have somehow created a society in which little concern is given to the needs of the society as a whole or the needs of the individual. We have forced ourselves to repress many normal and natural emotions.

For some, beginning to really feel these sentiments through the energy of the willow is not a good thing, for it takes time to sort these things out, and time is money. But look at the annual cost of medicines and treatments for the average citizen and you can see that this is an economic fallacy. A healthy society is measured through the health and happiness of the humblest of its people (the majority), not the most rich and powerful (the minority). To best use the transformational powers of the willow you may need to give yourself time. This emotional phase of healing is a necessary phase if you want to evolve as a spiritual being – one that requires great insight and courage – but it is a calling that we all get. We must suffer in order to grow as human beings, but the pain is worth it, for after the pain is understanding and clarity of action. We learn that all pain and suffering has its roots in desire.

Sitting under a willow tree will often give you feelings of melancholy, but this is not a bad thing. It gives us a reason to look inside and see what is lurking there and to bring it out into the light of day so that we may consummate and acknowledge these feelings.

Many years ago it was understood that anyone wearing a garland of willow was suffering emotionally and was treated with much respect and compassion. These people were helped through their time of crisis in a show of mutual respect for this universal experience. Rather than avoided and ignored, they were guided and supported.

Willows give you the ability to understand when it is important to bend with the wind like its branches or hold fast like its trunk.

Many native people tie feathers onto the extended, accepting branches of the willow, each feather representing a prayer sent to the heavens. This is generally done in winter.

It is believed that a person will recover more quickly if laid in a bed surrounded by fresh willow leaves. During the winter a few dried leaves may be placed in a saucer of water and set next to the patient. The leaves should be replaced every few days.

If you wish to attract a lover, try carrying a few leaves in a medicine pouch or bag and wear it around your neck. If that doesn't work, try casting seven dried willow leaves into a fire one at a time. Dedicate every leaf to each of the seven sacred directions. The first one is offered up to heaven and our Creator. The second is for our Mother the Earth. To each compass direction – East, North, West and South (in the southern hemisphere) – another leaf is thrown in the fire, giving thanks to these Adawees, the guardians of the four directions. The last leaf is dedicated to the heart, which is the centre of the universe. As the last leaf goes in, ask Spirit to bring someone into your heart and be a part of the sacred centre.

All parts of the willow are considered sacred and will act as your ally against evil deeds or thoughts from others or from inside yourself. Dried willow sticks make good clapper sticks; these may be struck together in a heart-beat rhythm to ward off negative influences. Sections of wood have also been fashioned into wind chimes that serve to protect houses from wind damage.

Seven sacred shrubs/vines

Artemisia
(*Artemisia*, many species)

There are few plants that grace a garden and better supply the apothecary than the extensive group of herbs known collectively as the artemisias. They have been known for centuries, not only for their curative power but for their ability to cleanse the mind, body and spirit. This genus of plants has been known throughout the recorded history of the Western world, appearing in almost every herbal book since Dioscorides wrote *De Materia Medica* in the first century. The name itself, *Artemisia* – a reference to Artemis, the Greek goddess of nature and the cycle of birth – indicates the spiritual essence believed to be inhabiting each member of this genus.

The three major species used in Western natural medicine are *A. absinthium*, commonly known as wormwood, *A. dracunculus*, which is called French tarragon, and *A. vulgaris* or mugwort. Although there are many other lesser known artemisias growing throughout Europe and the Mediterranean region, these three seem to have received most of the attention from herbalists. They are all useful in the treatment of stomach problems, warding off disease and infection, and in regulating delayed or irregular menstruation.

It would take an entire chapter to document adequately all of the uses these plants have participated in, and most herb books cover them at least in some detail. I will steer away from more conventional knowledge and deal primarily with the members of this genus that have for countless generations provided an assortment of cures for the physical and spiritual ailments amongst the native population of North America and Canada.

There are twenty-seven species of artemisia growing in North America and most of them are known collectively as sagebrush. Although many people confuse this with members of other plants called sage (*Salvia*), it is in no way related. I can only surmise that the name *sage* refers to the spiritual nature of both genera, in that they have all been used by sages, sorcerers, witches and spiritual healers from all corners of the world. Nowhere is this practice still maintained in a more sacred way than it is among Native Americans.

The use of artemisias along the eastern seaboard of America really only began when the first explorers and settlers brought European species over in the 1500s. Their herbal qualities, along with those of many other herb species, were shared with the indigenous people who in turn shared their knowledge with the ever-increasing white newcomers. The Indian population greatly appreciated this new gift from such a faraway land and in a very short time adapted many medical practices to accommodate these marvellous new herbs. Spreading from the east with the French and British colonization of America and from the west with the Spanish, these new artemisias augmented and occasionally replaced old medicines and practices. One of the best examples of this can be seen in California, where, in a few short decades, wormwood has completely replaced the use of sagebrush in protecting the winter stores of acorns against insect infestations. Both species did the job, but the Amerindians found wormwood a superior deterrent against grubs and weevils, and quickly adopted this practice. Although these new species added to the medical resources of the Native American pharmacopoeia, the use of sagebrush is still widespread in Native (and now non-Native) traditional culture.

PHYSICAL ASPECTS

Most species of artemisia are evergreen shrubs ranging in size from sixty centimeters to almost three meters. A few species, such as mugwort and tarragon, are more like perennials and a couple more are annuals. All have fragrant and interesting foliage, often in shades of grey or white, which lightens up any garden. Most produce small, abundant yellow flowers and although they set an incredible number of seeds, few become weedy. I suspect that many very small

insects consume them before fav-
ourable weather hastens germination in spring.

Most of the artemisias are sun-
lovers and should be planted in the
sunniest corner of the garden,
although they can tolerate partial
sun. They all thrive in well drained
soil and benefit from occasional
deep waterings. Once established, they can withstand long periods
of drought and neglect. I give my plants a good feed in spring and
again in late summer after they have bloomed, but they will still
grow in relatively infertile soil.

Most species are started from seed or by taking softwood or
semi-hardwood cuttings in the summer. Most of the seedlings are
extremely small and can only be handled once they are a few
months old.

MEDICINAL ASPECTS

Once again it would take at least a chapter to provide a truly com-
prehensive list of medical and spiritual practices involving this group
of plants, so I will concentrate on the species that I am most familiar with, and out of these half-dozen or so plants I will start with my
favorite, *A. tridentata*, the big basin sagebrush.

This is the legendary sagebrush of cowboy and Indian movie
fame, and few plants conjure up visions of life in the wide-open
spaces of the old West like this one. Known to the Navajo (Dine)
people as *Ts'ah*, it was (and still is) made into a beverage that was
taken before beginning a long journey or competing in any athletic
activities in the belief that it provided stamina and endurance.

Often the leaves would be placed at the bottom of moccasins to
keep the wearer's feet from blistering and to minimize corns and
calluses. Taken internally as a tea it relieved indigestion and other

stomach problems. Among the Navajo, as well as for the Paiute people of what is now Nevada (who called this plant *Sawabe*), it was also used as a mouthwash or gargle for sore throats and as a beautiful yellowish-green, almost golden, dye that was excellent for dyeing wool. It still plays an important role in almost every ceremony and is now sold in great quantities to non-Native people for smudging.

The white sage, *A. ludoviciana*, has been an equally important herb to the Amerindians living throughout the western parts of America and Canada, and northern Mexico. The botanical name refers to the vast area of land that was purchased from the French by the emerging United States in 1803 and extends from the Mississippi River to the Rocky Mountains. Called the Louisiana Purchase, this was probably one of the best land buys in history. One of the most interesting uses of this particular species was as a moxa. This is very similar to the Chinese practice of placing a small mound of dried foliage on the skin and setting it alight to heat up a blocked acupuncture point, thereby freeing up the flow of *Chi*. In some cases, a sharpened twig of sagebrush is inserted into the skin, just like an acupuncture needle, and is lit and allowed to burn down almost to the skin, at which point it is quickly pulled out.

The juice extracted from this plant is used to relieve the effects of poison oak. When blended into a salve of buffalo fat and applied to the skin, it was once said to be effective against eczema, whilst the fresh foliage was inserted into one nostril to ease headaches. I find that just rubbing fresh leaves in the palms of my hands and inhaling the fragrance for a few minutes is a good antidote for headaches, too.

Another species, *A. gnaphalodes*, or white mugwort as it is commonly called, was claimed to be a powerful antidote against poisoning and was also employed as a deodorant, for scenting a towel for drying oneself after a bath, and as a hair rinse that combats dandruff.

A. frigida has been taken for a variety of complaints, including convulsions, hemorrhages and irregular menstruation, and was once chewed as a heart medicine and said to revive comatose patients. As with most other species of sagebrush the smoke from the foliage was considered a highly effective disinfectant and was burned regularly whenever any infectious disease was present. Whereas white mugwort was called man-sage (*hetane' vano-estse*), *A. frigida* was prized as women's medicine (*Wia-ta-pezhihuta*) and was often made up into a tea and given to women who had just given birth to clear any afterbirth and cleanse the womb. The Californian species, *A. californica*, was used in much the same way, with women ceremonially drinking the tea from their first moon cycle to honor their new womanhood and then taken until menopause. It was also given to newborns to clear their respiratory system.

One last species I would like to cover is *A. campestrus*, which, when the root was made into a tea, had a reputation for loosening mineral obstructions to the urinary tract and clearing phlegm from the lungs and stomach. The powdered leaves were inhaled to relieve nosebleeds, whilst the smoke from the smoldering foliage drove away the hordes of mosquitoes that would come around at night. It was also the primary ceremonial drink given to women participating in their monthly four day moon lodge.

All these species have played a vital and important role in the lives of millions of human beings around the world. We also find this marvellous genus of plant in Africa (*A. afra*) and Asia (*A. annua*) where it is called *Qing hoa*; wherever it grows, it is used in the treatment of similar medical conditions.

Artemisia is the ultimate cleansing herb for the soul and for clearing the energy of many ceremonial objects and those of more utilitarian use such as bowls and cups. It is one of the best examples of the synchronistic herbal knowledge given to all people in all places. It was and always will be one of the greatest gifts ever placed on Earth for the benefit of all people.

SPIRITUAL ASPECTS

As we travel along this life-course that we have set for ourselves, we encounter more joy and more sorrow and disappointment. When we begin to dwell on what we view as negative experiences, we begin calling in a variety of energies that are attracted to these emotions, and in a way they actually begin feeding on the guilt, shame or anger. Fatalistic emotions draw these forces like moths to a candle and drain us of our life force. We sleep but are not rested; we eat but are unable to absorb the essence from our food. Those who work in spiritual healing know that there are entities that consume our worldly emotions and grow strong from our weaknesses. The best way to deal with these beings is to cleanse whatever they feed on.

This is the gift that is given to us by artemisia. The leaves of this plant possess the ability to send emotional parasites packing. Whether you use it fresh on your body or 'smudge' with the dried, smoldering foliage, the effect will be the same. You will feel a lifting of your etheric body as it becomes lighter, shedding the layers of negativity and self-abuse from your mental and emotional bodies. Just as smudge sticks were used to drive away biting insects from our homes, so can negative feelings be driven away from the dwelling of our soul.

In the Native American tradition, smudge sticks are first lit and the smoke is offered to the sacred directions. I choose to acknowledge seven directions: God, Earth, South, West, North, East and the centre of the universe, my heart. You may pay respect to however many directions you believe there are, for it is the intent rather than the content that is important. A feather is commonly used to waft the smoke over the body, particularly the seven points of power, or chakras, starting with the head or crown chakra and working down. The feather is believed to gently shift the aura in a way that allows more of the smoke to enter into the etheric body. In time you can learn to recognize areas in your auric field that are distorted or beginning to wear thin. These weak spots, once recognized, can be manipulated with the feather to correct the imbalance. The smoke acts like a 'filler' and helps protect the damaged aura until you can recognize the cause of the wound and repair it from the inside.

Using some form of artemisia should be a prerequisite before beginning any form of healing, whether you are healing yourself or others. I prefer common sagebrush, *A. tridentata*, for smudging, but this is my choice and you must make your own. If you find another species more to your liking, by all means use it. You will often be guided to the right one for you and should not get too caught up in what others are doing. Before you practice any healing, it is always beneficial not only to perform a cleansing of some sort, but also to offer up your prayers of gratitude in a cloud of artemisia smoke.

Many of us visit or live in houses that have negative sludge literally oozing from the walls and ceiling. The very nature of negative energy is that it is extremely sticky and will adhere to almost anything. In a dwelling where negativity is expressed often, whether outwardly or in a repressed manner, over time it builds up like soot. If you live in such a house and have rid yourself of the source of emotional sludge but feel that there is still some stuck to the surfaces, or if you are planning to move into such a home, it is usually beneficial to go through and give it a good smudging.

You may notice that the smudge stick is hard to light at times while at others it will go off like a roman candle and be hard to extinguish. This can be due to environmental factors, such as high humidity or dampness, or can indicate the stick's ability to judge the amount of cleansing needed. I do not believe that it is coincidence that, at a particular time when there was an increase in negative thoughts and actions in my house, a smudge stick that I had used and had thoroughly extinguished in sand decided to re-ignite and to fill the house with a thick blanket of smoke which triggered the smoke alarm. This is artemisia's way of telling you it's time for a good cleansing.

When preparing a bath, add foliage from the species of artemisia that appeals to you and it will help you wash away any negative feelings or emotions. Planting sagebrush or wormwood around the house will help guard against the 'bad' influences of others or any spells that have been cast your way.

Begin any ceremonies or communications with a smudging. Any time you must speak your truth to another individual or group, it is vital that you do so with a clean and clear heart and with the right intent. This is a positive, spiritual way of 'clearing the air', and I know that our system of government would flow much more quickly and smoothly if this practice were followed before each sitting of the Houses of Parliament.

A flower essence made from these plants when in bloom is good to use when your mind is cluttered with negative thoughts or emotions. A few drops under the tongue will help calm and relax you in times of stress, or you can use this sacred elixir in water-cleansing ceremonies when things get really critical. Starting with the crown chakra, place a few drops on each power point on your body and imagine all negativity being washed away.

Mugwort is commonly used in Asia to ward away evil spirits and is often hung in doorways to keep disease at bay. It is also said to promote prophetic dreams or visions if placed under the pillow or on your meditation altar. A mild tea of this herb is also good for washing any sacred objects such as crystals or wands. I have been told that a flower essence made from blooming mugwort can increase a person's chance of having twins or at least increase fertility in men.

Mugwort can also be woven into a belt and worn around the solar plexus to protect from evil forces of any kind. This is what John the Baptist is said to have worn when he was vision-questing in the wilderness.

If a small sprig of wormwood is added to liqueur and shared with someone you desire, they will find you most attractive. My experience is that any alcohol can have the effect of making you more attractive to others, as long as they are doing the drinking. In other words, the more you drink, the better I look.

Carrying a piece of sagebrush in your medicine pouch or bag will provide you with an aromatic reminder that you are being protected from negative vibrations or energies. Bracelets or anklets woven from sagebrush are worn during Sun Dance to purify those participating. These are very powerful medicine tools and are not for everyday use. If you attempt to weave your own, I would suggest that you be very sure that you are proceeding with the right intent.

Putting a small sprig of mugwort or sagebrush in your shoe will increase your endurance and make your road smoother.

Barberry

(*Berberis* and *Mahonia*, many species)

I know of few Grandmothers that are tougher, hardier and more useful than those represented in the genus *Berberis* and her close relation, the *Mahonia*. Both have been categorized by botanists as *Berberis*, or barberry, although now it is more correct to differentiate between the two. They are sisters and for that reason I will refer to them both as *Berberis*.

Species are found growing throughout Europe, Asia and North America, with *Mahonia* represented in the western third of the United States. They are, for the most part, a spiny lot, which says quite a bit if you are a follower of the Doctrine of Signatures. (This is a belief followed by indigenous people around the world which observes a relationship between the shape or color of a leaf, stem, root or flower, and the part of the body that is affected by the plant. Simplistically, a heart-shaped leaf may be beneficial to the heart whilst a lung-shaped leaf is obviously for the lungs.)

What does it mean, then, when a plant looks so threatening, exhibiting sharp thorns and rasp-like leaves? *Berberis* reminds us that healing can be quite painful; that occasionally we have to face the spines and barbs that are part of transformation of many kinds.

PHYSICAL ASPECTS

The plants that I have categorized as barberry are generally solid, upright and impenetrable shrubs. Some, like the common barberry (*B. vulgaris*), are deciduous while others, such as Magellan barberry (*B. buxifolia*) and Darwin barberry (*B. darwinii*), are evergreen. Several species are semi-deciduous. Most are very thorny and make excellent hedges and windbreaks. The foliage is often brightly colored, the best example being the red-leaf Japanese barberry (*B. thunbergii* 'Atropurpurea'), which is adorned with bronzy purple-red leaves throughout the summer months when the sun is at its strongest.

All species produce berries which range in color from orange to dark purple. The majority of shrubs reach about three meters although there are several species that grow to only sixty centimeters, such as the Japanese barberry.

The mahonias are of very different appearance to the barberries in that they have long, spineless stems that are topped with very prickly, holly-like foliage. They look like and are related to heavenly bamboo, *Nandina domestica*, and spread in a non-invasive way from underground stems. All species are evergreen and produce bright yellow flowers followed by blue or purple berries. The lowest growing plant is creeping mahonia (*M. repens*), which rarely surpasses one metre in height, while the tallest is probably the leather-leaf mahonia (*M. bealei*). The Oregon grape, *M. aquifolium*, reaches about two meters and in my biased opinion is the best looking of the lot. I also find the berries to be more palatable than those of other varieties.

Barberries and mahonias are very tolerant of conditions, growing in most positions throughout the temperate regions of Australia and New Zealand. Barberries are often more tolerant of full sun but will also do well in partial shade. The color of the foliage is improved by planting in direct sun. They are fast growers and occasional pruning will keep them more compact and bushy. Mahonias are slower growing and prefer to be planted in partial shade in fairly good soil but will also take less than ideal situations. They are all surprisingly drought resistant but appreciate regular deep watering in the heat of summer. All respond to regular organic fertilizing in early spring through to autumn.

Propagation is done mostly from cuttings, which are quite easily taken in summer. Seeds may also be started but are much slower and may need some stratification.

MEDICINAL ASPECTS

If we closely inspect the root and stem we see that they are yellow, particularly under the thin bark, and this reflects the pallor that the skin exhibits when the liver is not functioning fully and effectively or the gall bladder is inflamed, or both. Just as many infants develop jaundice in the first few months of life from the anger and pain of being born into such a noisy, polluted and confused world, so too are we overtaxing our liver to the state of exhaustion. When this occurs in a newborn we find the best medicine to be light from the sun. A newborn recognizes the sun for what it represents: the Light of Love from where all things are created. The child is then calmed and the liver begins to operate at capacity. We also benefit by allowing the sun's luminosity to wash over our skin and enter our etheric body. This conscious effort of bringing the light (love) into your life is well indicated by the barberries, in the golden yellow glow of bark and flower that they share with us, just for the joy of giving – the gift of cleansing our fear, shame and anger.

This idea of barberries representing light and love was echoed by those who dedicated their lives to the pursuit of the spiritual path and planted the shrub around churches and monasteries during the Middle Ages in Europe. This practice was most likely borrowed from the Druids who considered the barberry to be a sacred being manifested in the physical world to bring food, medicine and a rich yellow dye for leather and cloth. Once there were vast areas of barberry (*B. vulgaris*) growing throughout Europe, but due to wheat fields and an unfair persecution by farmers in an effort to rid their wheat crops of rust, the occurrence of barberry was reduced to hedgerows and home gardens, where it was used more to provide fruit for jams, jellies and preserves.

Many folk medicines call on barberry bark, particularly the root bark, for congested liver problems, as a general blood cleanser and tonic and in treating diarrhea. In the Mediterranean area, many thousands of years before modern science isolated berberine and found it to be effective against many bacterial agents, fennel was combined with the bark and brewed into a syrup that was said to help stave off infectious diseases. It has also been shown to stimulate involuntary muscles. Berberine is still found in modern eye drops, a legacy of knowledge that was acquired by what many people now look upon as ignorant savages who practiced witchcraft and worshiped nature spirits.

On the other side of the Atlantic grow many native species of *Berberis* which for centuries have provided the native American community with a plethora of medical and utilitarian benefaction.

The most common species before the introduction of European barberry to the continent was *B. canadensis*, or bush pepper to the Cherokee people, who used it to 'check loose bowels' (as it was phrased so nicely). Many other tribes employed the leaves and bark as 'old women's medicine' and gave it to elderly grandmothers to keep their liver, spleen and gall bladder in good working order. Barberry bark and root were also administered for migraines, a rare occurrence in the old days. Many nations living in what is now called New England, such as the Mohegan and Penobscot, have traditionally made up a cold decoction of the fruit to treat tonsillitis and sore throats and reduce the accompanying fever. The powdered root bark was applied directly to mouth ulcers.

Further to the west we find that most of the species are now categorized under *Mahonia*, although there is still confusion about the names. I know of about eight species of *Mahonia*, and there is one, *M. nevinii*, which may be extinct in the wild. *M. fremontii*, which grows from Northern California to the Rocky Mountains, has an ancient history of use. The Hopi and Navajo (Dine) people of the south-west found it useful in treating indigestion and the accompanying symptoms such as heartburn and stomach ache. The Ute, Cheyenne, Paiute and many other nations mixed the bark in fat as a lotion to cover infected cuts or wounds and as a dressing to soothe skin eruptions. As the skin is often an indication of the state of the liver, it is safe to say that they had the right idea. For minor injuries, the root was simply chewed and applied to the site. It was also used as a hangover cure by those who indulged in 'whiteman's fire-water'.

M. repens, appropriately called creeping mahonia, was known to the Paiute as *ch cow cow* and the root was pounded, steeped in water and applied to hemorrhoids. Many people believed that it had the power to cure certain cancers, most likely those of the stomach and liver. The leaves were even chewed for acne and boiled into a tea for rheumatic pain and general muscular discomfort. The Salish (Flat-head) and Kutenai Indians of north-western America and south-western Canada considered this plant to be more of a kidney tonic and as a cure for consumption. It was also administered after child-birth to help expel the placenta and may have been useful in treating stomach ulcers. There have been reports of its having been used as a contraceptive, but I wouldn't want to start experimenting on just how one would use it.

I've saved my favorite for the last, and that is the Oregon grape, *M. aquifolium*. The common name is misleading, because it is not a grape and Oregon is only one of its natural habitats. It grows naturally in one of my favorite haunts, the Pacific north-west. It has all the medicinal attributes of its counterparts, but to me it has a special quality and significance. This is impossible to define other than to say that this plant has given me much help throughout my adult life. She is a friend and a healer, and even at my current home in Gembrook, Victoria, she is still very much a part of my life.

Virtually every Indian tribe living in close proximity to this shrub used it for every ailment, from ringworm to chronic coughs. The bright yellow color that was extracted from the bark and roots was used to dye buckskins and fabrics as well as baskets and other every-day items. The ash from the wood was mixed with water and applied to the scalp to dye the hair yellow for battle, although there were rarely any wars.

The blue-black berries were relished by the local population, especially after white settlers introduced sugar to the Indian diet. Before sugar was used they were most often mixed with meat or dried for later use. They are still used in jams and jellies, and make a refreshing drink when mixed in cool water. The Karok tribe subscribed to the unusual belief that the berry was poisonous and they employed it only to paint their arrow shafts. My feeling is that they were showing respect by not eating the berries that helped make their arrows fly so straight and true. Besides, many other berries were far more palatable than the rather sour barberry. I have heard that roasting the berries over a fire makes them sweeter, but haven't tried it.

The fruit was known to have a cooling effect on the body and was given to reduce fevers and stimulate the appetite.

SPIRITUAL ASPECTS

Now, more than any other time in history, we are forced to filter great quantities of pollution and anger and in doing so are seriously threatening our lives and our planet.

Through the use of the physical and etheric qualities of *Berberis* we can now begin to work on those things that continually jab at our subconscious: issues, fears and challenges. By using the root of these fine plants we can begin the process of cleansing our bodies, the tea or tincture being the catalyst for changing our perspective on the problems we face. Just as our physical liver filters impurities and pollutants out of our bodies, so too does the etheric liver filter out our emotional impurities and pollutants.

As *Berberis* performs her task of cleansing our liver and blood of toxins, we are often faced with many of the emotional, mental and spiritual issues that have been buried deep within, for it is the liver that filters anger and many other negative emotions from our system.

Also, as the medicine begins to work, it is important to bring into view, through meditation and inner reflection, a realization that the dilemmas we create are here to teach us and to make us better human beings. This realization is represented by the sharp spines that characterize the genus. They serve not to injure but to protect. Just as the spines of the barberry serve to protect the small birds as they feed on the ripe berries, by keeping foraging animals at bay, so too do we use our spines of anger to protect us from emotional 'browsers' who seek to take too much and give too little. We repress many things in our lives to protect our psyche from threat. As you work with this genus, think about which barbs you need to keep for self-preservation, and which can be discarded so that you pose no threat to those who wish you only love, comfort and compassion.

An excellent way to bring this into the physical is to gather a number of barberry thorns or the prickly leaves of mahonia and glue or paste each one onto an individual piece of paper – one spine or leaf per piece. Then begin writing down things that make you really angry, or a past event that still creates that anger. As you write, reflect on how that anger has served you and how it has kept you from being closer to others. Keep looking at the thorn that is attached to your piece of paper and try to connect as many things as you can to the actual emotion or event.

As you begin to understand the true nature and lesson to be learned from those stimuli that make you angry, you may find it useful to write a letter to the person you feel responsible for the pain you felt and thank them for the gift of self discovery and understanding. Then fold the paper into a medicine bundle and wait for the night of the new moon. Build a fire with intent – that is, a fire that you have started with a specific purpose in mind. When you build a fire with intent, you empower it to work with you in the healing process or to bring in good spirits or bring you wisdom or the power of prophetic vision. Make the intent of this fire the desire to reduce your anger to ash just as a fire transforms a dark, heavy piece of wood to the lightest of materials. Cast into this fire of intent your paper medicine bundle and watch as the paper, the writing and the leaves or thorns are consumed. Give thanks for the strength to turn your anger into learning and your barbs into the light of the wisdom fire.

Another attribute that mahonia plants possess is the ability to bring financial abundance to those who carry a piece of the root. When carrying this amulet it is important to remember that acquiring abundance requires that it be spread around to benefit all.

One of the best places to meditate is in an area where mahonias are growing. Their energy helps us to filter the toxins that continue to plague our thoughts and keep us from reaching a deep meditative state. Imagine the golden yellow glow of her bark and flowers and the light of the sun stored deep in her roots that bring brightness into an anger-filled liver. Focus on the golden light of love and forgiveness that is radiated outward from this plant and cleanses our etheric body. Picture your entire body glowing with this golden color and see the golden pathway that exists between you and this sacred Grandmother. May she bring you peace and tranquillity.

Elder
(Sambucus, many species)

It was the custom in not-so-long-ago Europe to doff your hat or cap when passing an elderberry bush. This was done out of a healthy respect for the power of this plant to cure or to make very sick. It was thought that, if the spirit that inhabits this plant took a dislike to you, she would purge you like you've never been purged before.

Indeed, elderberry bushes have been venerated since we became human beings and they have always commanded a great deal of respect and been utilized for many medical and spiritual purposes.

This plant yields almost a full spectrum of colors: green dye from the leaves, red, blue or purple dye from the fruit, black dye from the roots and brown from the bark.

The Yukon Indians found the stems to be ideal for measuring out burial plots. On a lighter note, many Native American people fashioned flutes from the dried, hollowed-out stems, a practice that was also followed by the Greeks, who gave the elder her botanical name *Sambucus* (from the Greek word *sambuke*, which means 'a musical pipe'). The hollowed stem also served as a handy tool with several uses – for tapping syrup from maple trees, as spindles in weaving and even as a ceremonial cutting device for severing the umbilical cord – and as a toy: the Meskwake and Pawnee children made it into squirt guns and toy pop guns to play with.

PHYSICAL ASPECTS

Elders for the most part are considered shrubs or shrub-like trees. At least one species, *Sambucus ebulus*, the dwarf elder or danewort, is a spreading perennial rarely growing higher than one metre. The red berries are considered poisonous. Large clusters or umbels of white or cream-colored flowers are fol-lowed by blue, purple or red fruit, depending on species. All elders are deciduous. They prefer moist environments that provide at least some cooling shade. They are not fussy about soil type, as long as it is not sodden. All enjoy an early spring fertilizing and regular deep soaks. Prune out old stems in winter to promote new growth.

MEDICINAL ASPECTS

Although much of the plant is considered toxic when taken internally, it has nonetheless been used as medicine for eons. **As all parts of the plant contain some highly toxic substances, such as cyanagenic glycosides, they should all be considered poisonous, particularly when fresh.** Now that I've scared you a little, I will point out that elder has always been an important herbal medicine when administered correctly, but it is one of the plants that will sicken you if the right intent, knowledge and respect are not there.

Native Americans throughout the United States and Canada regularly used it internally. Most commonly the flowers were used in a tea for sweating out fevers, a treatment shared by the Menominee, Cherokee and many others. It was usually given at the first signs of cold or 'flu and followed by a trip to the sweat lodge. The Mohegans made a weak tea for colic whilst others drank it to induce vomiting, a popular practice amongst many Amerindians when unwell. The flowers have also been taken for upper respiratory conditions, a remedy shared by the Gypsies scattered throughout Europe.

The bark played an important role in Amerindian medicine, although specific skills had to be used to scrape off the bark. If you were after a medicine that would make the patient 'cleanse from within' (as 'throwing up' is often termed), you would scrape the bark from the bottom of the stem to the top. If you needed to cure other ailments, such as arthritis, rheumatism, mouth ulcers or epilepsy, you would scrape from top to bottom. Even the size of the stem or branch was an important consideration, often measured as the same as the distance between the patient's second and third finger joints.

In extreme cases of arthritis or rheumatism, Yukon medicine men applied a dried, smoldering stem on the affected area of the body and allowed it to burn all the way down, dressing the burned area of the skin with medicinal ointments.

The leaves, often mixed with the flowers, were applied externally as a poultice for infections and headaches and on bruises and sprains. Leaves and stems were swept over floors, in storage areas and over vegetable crops and fruit trees in the belief that this would repel mice and insects.

The Illinois and Miami Indians boiled the roots and bark and added them to soup for 'failing arms', whatever that was.

The fruit, which is high in vitamin C, has been cooked in pies, jams and jellies, fermented into wine (for medicinal purposes, of course), gargled for sore throats, made into syrup for coughs and brewed to treat constipation. Generally, fruits that are blue or purple are safe to eat, while caution must be used if ingesting red ones.

SPIRITUAL ASPECTS

Archaeologists tell us that the elderberry shrub played a significant role in the lives of Stone Age people living in Europe. Evidence indicates that it was transplanted and cultivated near the dwellings of these people to protect the occupants from evil and was said to ward off lightning. I have heard that there was one planted outside Westminster Abbey for at least one of these purposes. The elder is also said to promote longevity.

The great wealth of legend associated with elder is far too vast to cover here, so I will give you a few personal tips I have learned. The first wisdom about Grandmother Elder was taught to me by the gentle Paiute and Washoe who once shared my old home, Lake Tahoe, during the summer food-gathering time. In those days, leisure time was just as important as work time and the best way to relax was to have a smoke. First, it was necessary to find a dried-out section of elder stem and remove any remaining pith so that it was completely hollow. This stem was then filled with the preferred smoking mix – in my case, the inner bark from the red-twig dogwood (*Cornus stolonifera*), the flaking bark and dried leaves from kinnikinnik or bear berry (*Arctostaphylos uva-ursi*) and a touch of secret stuff. The best part about this 'pipe' was that one had to lie down on one's back to smoke it. This inactivity taught me many things. I learned to appreciate just watching the sky and thinking of nothing else but the beauty and vastness of it all, to rediscover the comfort of touching my full body to the Earth and sharing in her abundance, and to respect my elders.

Elder wood is a sacred and powerful medicine which, if carried, will help to turn away any evil deeds or thoughts. The leaves are good for creating protection for anyone or anything. Scattered to the four directions they bring blessing and good fortune and will ward away spells and such. To relieve insomnia, try putting a few elderberries under your pillow, preferably dried unless you want to tie-dye your sheets.

Whistles and flutes can be made from the dried, hollowed-out wood and used to call nature spirits. It is best to call after midnight when you can get off-peak rates!

Raspberries and blackberries
(Rubus, many species*)*

No plant more powerfully calls me back to my early days of learning about the foods and medicines of my mountain home in the Sierras than the raspberry. Back then I was far more interested in self-sufficiency, growing my own fruits, vegetables and rooting around for wild foods.

A friend of mine who had terrible menstrual cramps asked me whether I knew anything that would help relieve her condition. Being the intrepid mountaineer, and not wanting her to think that I was completely insensitive to women's problems, I told her I would go out and gather something from the bush that would indeed help her. Of course I didn't have a clue what to give her, much less how to go and gather it, so I drove down to the local health-food shop and asked the woman behind the counter what she would use for such a condition. Law forbade her from recommending anything to anyone, but she took me over to the book section and let me have a bit of a read.

It didn't take long to find many references to red raspberry leaves as being of real benefit to sufferers of pre-menstrual pain, and I quickly bought a large bag of dried leaves. The next day I visited my friend with the 'newly harvested leaves' and told her to drink three cups of leaf a day, just like the books had said. Within a few months her symptoms had all but disappeared and I was a hero. This was perhaps not the best way to get into the world of herbs, but Spirit never cares how you get into a worthy pursuit as long as you do it. Now, many years later, I have learned of the many other attributes that this common plant has to offer.

In virtually every temperate region on Earth raspberries and blackberries thrive and have provided food and medicine since humanity was dragging its knuckles through the Pleistocene Age. In most areas it was not only the leaves that were considered medicinal. Virtually every part has some purpose, whether to heal the physical or deal with those in Spirit.

PHYSICAL ASPECTS

Most raspberries and blackberries are considered perennial shrubs with biennial branches and are deciduous during winter, or at least partly so. They often spread through underground runners and rooting branches, and grow to approximately two meters. All bear edible fruit in spring or summer and occasionally in autumn.

MEDICINAL ASPECTS

The dried leaves, decocted in boiling water as a tea, can be given to women in their first trimester of pregnancy. They are said to tone and strengthen the uterine lining and are also recommended for post-partum bleeding, to help in childbirth and to ease pre-menstrual pain. Tea made from the leaves has been reliable as a treatment for diarrhea and dysentery, as a kidney cleanser and for cleaning bile and blood.

The Iroquois brewed a combination of blackberry and strawberry roots which was given to people of all ages as a spring cleaner, and a mash of the blackberry root was applied to the irritated navels of infants. Cherokees, who call the red raspberry plant *yun-oo-go-s-ti*, chewed the roots to relieve coughs and bronchial congestion; whilst the Ojibwa decocted a tea for stomach pains and as a wash for sore eyes. Virtually every tribe had their own use for blackberries and raspberries and in the mountains we relished the fruit and healing properties of the little thimbleberry, *Rubus parviflorus*. The fruits could be dried for winter use or made into delicious jams or jellies. Being slightly diuretic and with a mild laxative effect, they helped keep everything running smoothly during the sluggish winter months. Fresh, they are all among the best of the berries, with the added bonus of ridding your teeth of tartar while you are eating.

SPIRITUAL ASPECTS

To look at a blackberry bramble one might believe that the Grandmother spirit that inhabits this plant must certainly be a prickly one indeed, for she seems to tempt you with her delicious reward but then attacks without mercy when you try to reap the harvest. True, she guards her fruit wisely, but not without reason.

There was a time long ago when the blackberry grew more like her sister the raspberry, with softer thorns and more upright form. But her fruit was much to the liking of the people who lived back then, and they came from far and wide to taste it. So many people came that she was unable to give her friends the birds any of her crop, and as a result she conceived no babies. To make matters worse, the people were trampling her underfoot to secure the last of the berries and her new shoots were broken off and destroyed. The Creator, He-wen-i-yu, saw what was happening and placed a finger gently where the poor mangled blackberry was holding on to life. Suddenly the earth erupted with blackberry shoots until she grew as a great, impenetrable thicket. Now people could not damage her as before and she has spread around the world so that her life, and the lives of her young, can never be threatened again. The birds were happy, too, and composed a new song for the blackberry, which you can hear today when they feed on her luscious berries.

Working with this Grandmother opens up our consciousness about the rhythm of death and rebirth. We see that the fruit is borne on stems that will begin to die once the fruit has ripened and left the vine. The old growth recedes as the new comes forth. The world is turned over to a new generation and the old go willingly back to the Earth. When this cycle is broken, as it is in our human world, we become an unbalanced society. Birth and death become objects of fear and cause many people to reject both.

In women this fear can often manifest itself in the uterus as monthly pain and can even lead to miscarriage. In men, it can manifest itself as diarrhea, as we literally and figuratively crap our pants in fear.

Through observing the growth of this plant and partaking in her medicinal and vibrational qualities, we begin, both men and women, to find our place once again in the cycle of life. She strengthens our will and calms our fears. When we taste her fruit, we are tasting life. When we make a tea from her roots or leaves we begin to live again, not out of fear of death but in the joy of life.

It is an old Indian belief that if a man and woman share the fruit of the blackberry, they will be forever faithful to one another and never stray. Some people also believe that hanging a blackberry stem over the door will keep out unwanted spirit visitors. On a final note, it is well known that washing your dog in water that contains the crushed roots from a blackberry stem will make it a great hunter.

Rose

(*Rosa,* many species)

When I see a rose, and I see them often, I am drawn back to a time when my life seemed at an end.

At only twenty-two I had already served two and a half years in the United States Air Force, with one year spent in Vietnam and the rest spent resisting the war efforts. Needless to say, I didn't make a very good airman and found myself being booted out of the Intelligence Division, getting demoted and ending up as a base gardener. This was as low as one could get in the Air Force, but at least it afforded me sunshine and plenty of fresh air.

One of my first jobs was to help prune roses. I was puzzled when I saw one of the senior gardeners take some of the cut rose stems and shove them half way into the earth. He told me, as he did this, anticipating my question, that some of those sticks would actually grow roots and produce another rose identical to its 'parent'.

From that moment, something clicked into place, and for the rest of the winter I watched those cuttings, waiting for something to happen. Winter ended and those pieces of rose stems transformed into small but actively growing rose bushes.

And as they sprouted new life, so did I, for my own long emotional winter seemed to lift and the sun seemed to shine warmly for the first time in many years. I became a gardener, a horticulturalist and a herb grower, and I owe it all to the spirit of the rose which, when I needed it most, provided me with love, beauty and a renewed appreciation of life.

PHYSICAL ASPECTS

A large genus of mostly deciduous plants, roses are often grown ornamentally as ground covers, shrubs or climbing brambles. All bear striking flowers and orange rose hips which often persist throughout winter. The shrubs reach about two meters in height, while climbing varieties can cover a house if left unchecked.

MEDICINAL ASPECTS

As with many ornamental plants that grace our gardens, the rose can trace its connection to humans through its initial use as a medicinal herb and food source. It would probably be fair to say that, wherever they grew, the rose hips were utilized as a source of vitamin C. I was taught to gather the hips after a few good frosts (which I was told not only made the fruit more palatable, but increased the vitamin C content). Three rose hips are said to have the equivalent of one orange, and although I much prefer the latter, I have yet to find a way to dry and store oranges for any length of time, as I can with rose hips. They also make a palatable tea which I have found effective in treating symptoms of 'flu. I am told it is also good for combating tuberculosis, but I have never had the opportunity to try it. I have, however, found a weak decoction useful in soothing tired and inflamed eyes and as a wash for troublesome areas of the skin that constantly feel itchy or are irritated.

The roots provided virtually all Native American nations with medicine for many different ailments, including diarrhea, upset stomachs, sore throats, tonsillitis and colds, and (mixed with other herbs) acted as a general tonic. The dried bark of the root can be used on its own or mixed with tobacco or kinnikinnik as a smoking agent, whilst the inner bark was once made into a yellow dye for fabrics, baskets and hides. The dried roots and stems are considered to be an astringent and helpful in clotting blood.

Virtually every part of the plant can be used for one affliction or another. The Cherokee rose, *Rosa laevigata*, which the Cherokee people knew nothing of until it was introduced from China into parts of their original homeland, is still used in Asia to treat semen problems in men.

The most common use of the rose comes from the petals of the flower, which have been used by just about everyone in the 'civilized' world as a perfume and skin aid. They can also be made into decoctions for diarrhea and dysentery, as a general restorative and in the treatment of gonorrhea, although this latter cure has been superseded by a trip to the health clinic and a good dose of antibiotics.

SPIRITUAL ASPECTS

All human beings know that every living thing has its own song. Many of us have forgotten what our song is or even how to receive it, so we lose the ability to harmonize with the rest of the universe. The importance of knowing one's song is a concept that goes deep into the Native American spiritual philosophy. To live your life without a song is to live only partially. If we cannot add our song to the celestial Music of the Spheres, I believe, we are cut off from that which binds all things together. To share this concept, I find that the following passage best conveys the Amerindian view of this shrub. It is from an English translation, by Dr A McG Beede, of a traditional Dakota song called 'The Song of the Wild Rose'.

From the heart of the Mother we come,

The kind Mother of Life and of all;

And if ever you think she is dumb,

You should know that flowers are her songs.

And all creatures that live are her songs,

And all creatures that die are her songs,

And the winds blowing by are her songs,

And she wants you to sing all her songs.

Like the purple in Daydawn we come,

And our hearts are so brimful of joy

That whene'er we're not singing we hum

Ti-li-li-li-i, ta-la-la-la-loo, ta-la-la-la-loo!

When a maiden is ready to wed

Pin wild roses all over her dress,

And a rose in the hair of her head;

Put new moccasins onto her feet.

Then the heart of the Mother will give

Her the songs of her own heart to sing;

And she'll sing all the moons she may live,

Ti-li-li-li-i, ta-la-la-la-loo, ta-la-la-la-loo!

I was given my first song not through marriage but when I was able to open my heart to healing. It was the roses growing in the middle of a military installation that brought me this great gift: through their luxuriant green leaves, fresh in spring, and in the beauty of sight and fragrance of the flowers.

If you feel ready to reconnect with the Earthmother, then it is time to learn your first song. Find yourself a quiet place where there is a rose bush, or several rose bushes, preferably an older variety, bred before the 1950s. Many newer hybrids seem to lack the level of 'musical vibrations' owing to the fact that most new roses are bred for unusual colors or growth characteristics rather than for any spiritual essence. The older varieties also have the benefit of being easily propagated from hardwood cuttings taken in winter and are therefore readily shared with others.

After centering yourself, use the Golden Pathway meditation technique (see page 45) to better align yourself to the plant's vibrations. It is often helpful to beat a drum or clappers in time to a slow heartbeat while listening for your song. It is also important not to feel self-conscious or shy about using your voice, for it was given to you to better express your soul. You may find it helpful just to start humming whatever comes through. Some of it will be random notes, but the longer you allow yourself to flow with it, the more you will begin to notice certain combinations of notes being voiced, and with patience you should settle in on your sacred song. For some this comes naturally whilst others of us may struggle to let go enough to receive it, but everyone has the ability and receptiveness to make it happen.

If you're having trouble finding a suitable lover, try making a necklace from dried rose hips, or a piece of rosewood, and wear it when you are likely to encounter those of the appropriate gender. If you can then get them into an intimate bath with some rose oil, you stand a much better chance of making the relationship work. I suppose that could be said for any couple that shares a bath, rose oil or not.

Viburnum
(*Viburnum,* many species)

Cramp bark, black haw, devil's shoestring, stag bush, withe-rod and American sloe are just some of the common names given this lovely and useful group of shrubs that make up the genus of *Viburnum*.

The year-old branches from the arrow wood, *Viburnum acerifolium*, were often employed by many Indian nations in making arrows.

PHYSICAL ASPECTS

Most viburnums are shrubs known for their often fragrant clusters of white flowers in spring. There are both deciduous and evergreen species, growing to a height of five to seven meters. Many species have colorful autumn foliage and red berries which persist into winter.

MEDICINAL ASPECTS

Only one of the common names, cramp bark, alludes to the fact that this popular group of often-used landscape plants was one of the most commonly used herbs of midwives, medicine women and witches in the treatment of women's complaints on both sides of the

Atlantic. The bark of these deciduous shrubs has provided women
for countless generations with
relief from the sometimes debili-
tating pain of menstruation, or
moon-time as I prefer to call it.

As I described earlier in the
book, it was common practice for
most indigenous cultures to allow
the women to attend a moon
lodge or at least sleep and eat in separate quarters during their
moon-time, not because they were 'unclean', but to allow them
gently to pass through the veils that separate us from the world of
Spirit. This is a very special and sacred time when women are half
'here' and half 'there'. Without the support of family, friends and
community moon-time can become a painful, stressful experience
that often leaves a woman exhausted, drained (literally and figuratively) and often feeling guilty at having to make apologies to those
she loves.

With the aid of the viburnums and the support of a self-empower-
ing medical and social system, the monthly cycle has a chance to be a
time of great cleansing and insight, and women are far more likely to
endure childbirth with minimal discomfort. To my knowledge, every
cultural region has its share of herbs that serve this purpose, but for
the people living throughout Europe and eastern North America,
viburnum served this and many other medical conditions.

Although the leaves were occasionally applied externally to
inflamed tumors and in relieving migraines, it was the bark that was
revered as a uterine tonic; in the treatment of diarrhea, dysentery,
heart conditions, asthma; and as a diuretic. A decoction was often
given to women in the last trimester of pregnancy to help reduce
labor pains and staunch any excess hemorrhaging after birth. It was
also taken as a precaution against miscarriage. During the horrible

days of slavery in America, plantation owners often forced female slaves to drink this tea to counteract any effort the women might make to terminate an unwanted pregnancy through the use of cotton plant root.

According to the Iroquois, if you scraped the bark in an upward direction it would cleanse the blood and reduce a fever, whereas if the bark was scaped downward, it would act as a laxative. Many Native Americans also smoked the bark, usually in some mixture or combination of herbs, but occasionally by itself. Several Native American tribes living in what is now known as New England found the root useful in treating mumps.

Although some species of viburnum produce fruit that is pleasantly edible, it is best to assume that these berries are toxic unless cooked or unless you are otherwise instructed.

SPIRITUAL ASPECTS

We live in an age in which everything seems turned around. Many men are confused about the new role they are to play as we enter the new millennium and move firmly into the Fifth World, whilst women seek to reassert their power to be anything they wish to be without losing their feminine identity.

Spiritually we are at the point of learning how to incorporate the polarity of our male and female sides into a singularity, a more balanced and fulfilled being. In the confusions we see around us today we can witness the struggle that we must experience if we are to break free from the bonds of separated lives which force men to abandon all aspects of their feminine side and women to feel threatened for showing their male side. Men and women both stand to gain when this transformation is completed because each may share in the abundance of their fullness and bring a new sense of completeness to all.

The viburnums radiate an energy that helps open up blocked channels of communication with our higher selves. In Spirit we are all genderless, or, more accurately, we are the perfect balance of male and female energy. When you begin to acknowledge your opposite in the physical, it can often cause fear, tension and distress. For women this can manifest itself as unusually painful moon-times whilst for men it can settle into the base of the stomach where there are periodically painful episodes. Both are symptoms of the same emotional issues, and the viburnums offer us the vibrational tool that will help both sexes to overcome the obstacles that obscure our path. Using the herb, tincture or flower essence of, or simply meditating next to, one of these fairly common, white-flowering shrubs will help you overcome obstacles blocking the flow of your progression in life.

Finally, women are just beginning to rediscover the spiritual significance of their moon-time, and exhibiting the type of respect that has connected women so closely with the Earth since the dawn of humanity. The Earth receives much of her healing energy from the exchange of blood and pain from women during childbirth and their moon cycle. While men must subject themselves to rituals such as the Sun Dance, sweat lodge, vision quest and other pain-inducing, blood-letting endeavors to connect in this way, women have received the gift of life and have traditionally given thanks for this precious endowment by sharing their moon-induced blood with the Earthmother. All plants benefit from this returning of life-blood back into the soil, but few more than the viburnum. It will in turn increase its auric field and the intensity at which it resonates, and help heal all those men and women willing to take the time to open themselves to its radiant glory.

Vitex
(*Vitex agnus-castus* and others)

There are many herbs which, although known for centuries, have only now begun to come into their fullest potential. Perhaps it is just that we have become more thorough in our investigation of the chemical constituents of these plants and have a better understanding of the effect they have on our bodies. Or perhaps, as I believe, these loving beings have an ability to change their fundamental biochemistry so as to meet the new medical challenges that face us as we evolve as humans. Either way, vitex is one of those herbs that now brings us new hope in healing the imbalances we have created on the Earth and within our bodies in the mindless drive to consume her precious resources without regard to the consequences.

PHYSICAL ASPECTS

The best known species of *Vitex, V. agnus-castus*, is a deciduous shrub, sometimes a small tree growing up to eight meters. The foliage consists of delicate, deeply divided palmate leaves. The lavender-blue flowers are borne on panicles in late summer and autumn, followed by small fruit.

MEDICINAL ASPECTS

The cost of our material progress has been great. It is one that we will be repaying for many years to come, not only financially, but in the way we must now live our lives and in the manner in which our mental and physical health has been affected. In the process of trying to create a better world for ourselves, we have polluted our food and water resources to the point where it has become a health hazard to eat or drink.

We are constantly introducing into our bodies chemicals such as oestrogenic compounds, which have altered our delicate hormonal balances. Nowhere is this more evident than in the health issues that women now face. Hormonal imbalance has reached epidemic proportions, and the price we are paying is seen in the dramatic increase in the percentage of women suffering from irregular and often painful menstruation, depression, the growth of unwanted facial hair and even in the number of women having difficulty making the transition, physically and emotionally, through menopause.

It is no mere chance that *Vitex* has only now emerged as a valuable tool in combating these problems. The chaste tree, *Vitex agnus-castus*, has been employed for centuries in treating many ailments, including uterine inflammation, epilepsy, colic flatulence and 'insanity', and in reducing sexual desire in men. It was this latter use of the plant that gave rise to the common name of chaste tree, for the seeds were commonly given to Christian monks to dampen their sexual urges.

It has only been in the latter part of the twentieth century, however, that vitex has truly evolved into an effective tool in helping women re-establish the hormonal balance that has been lost through the excessive intake of pesticides, industrial pollution and birth control pills. All of these factors have contributed to an unhealthy excess of oestrogen in women. This is where vitex comes into her true power, for it is within the leaves and fruit that substances related to progesterone are found, and it is these compounds that can counteract the imbalances. In addition to helping women correct irregularities in their monthly cycles and stimulate lactation in nursing mothers, recent tests have also shown it to be useful in easing the physical and emotional problems associated with menopause.

Although this elegant, deciduous shrub (sometimes considered a small tree) is often referred to as a 'woman's herb', it is not uncommon to find modern applications that are helpful to men as well. I must say that there is little evidence that it really does quell male sexual desire; in fact, there are those who believe that it does just the opposite. My feeling is that it will affect each man differently but appropriately. In other words, for those who have a real need to decrease their libido, it will do just that; whilst in those men who wish to kick-start the libido it will perform in that way. As in women, it is simply a hormonal regulator and will correct any imbalances. It is also taken by males and females to control acne, particularly in teenagers.

This is a very safe herb and can be taken in conjunction with other synergistic herbs such as our old friend cramp bark, wild yam, blue or black cohosh (or both) and *dong quai* (Chinese angelica).

SPIRITUAL ASPECTS

There was a time when it was difficult for me to relate to 'women's business'. It wasn't that I didn't care about some of the health issues that face women, but rather, I just didn't have any frame of reference to go by. It was all a great mystery, and I'm afraid compassion and empathy were not one of my stronger points.

Then, several years ago, it was suggested to me by a great teacher and spiritual 'benefactor' that in order for me to be any kind of healer, it would be necessary to cultivate a better understanding of the enigmatic nature of these strange creatures, and the only way to do that, I was told, would be for me to 'get in touch with my feminine side'.

Of course, in those days I didn't have a clue what or where my feminine side was, much less how to get in touch with it. It appeared to be an impossible task, but one that I took on only because it seemed so important to my teacher. For the next few years I tried everything from meditation to mediation with little success, until I met my first vitex.

She was a lovely sight: five foot two with flowers of blue and palmate leaves that seemed to reach out to touch me. It was love at first sight. I had encountered few plants that had such a strong feeling of femininity, grace and strength. I soon found that working with this herb seemed to spark in me some strange sense of knowing, as if there was a part of me deep inside that was calling to me for release. Meditating next to her began to stir something in me, and as time went by, I truly felt as if there was indeed a hidden aspect of myself that I had never recognized before. This was my feminine side, and I came to understand that all men possess this quality just as all women have a male side that struggles to come forth. It is easier to comprehend knowing that, in spirit, we are never one gender or another but an amalgamation of these two energies.

From that first meditation I was hooked. This inborn female energy brought me a fullness I had not experienced before, and I continue to this day in my quest to maintain the balance. Contrary to what you might think, it does not lessen my manhood but augments it. It has enabled me to be a better communicator and far more able to experience a complete life.

This is the spiritual gift that vitex has to share with us.

It is said that carrying a piece of vitex wood in your pocket or medicine bag, or simply drilled and worn around the neck, will help you to reincorporate your two sides into a more total union. The pepper-like seeds are also good spiritual medicine and work in much the same way as the wood.

Seven sacred flowers

Amaranth

(*Amaranthus*, many species)

This colorful annual is known by a variety of names, such as Joseph's coat, love-lies-bleeding, prince's feather, tampala and pygmy torch.

To the Aztec nation of central Mexico, the amaranth was a great gift from the Creator, given to supply these people with food, medicine and a spiritual conduit through which there could always be communion and communication with the world of Spirit. No plant was more revered than this brightly colored flowering annual and it was the most widely grown plant in their realm. The dark, blood-red seed provided a nutritious source of grain that was made into bread, cakes and cereal; whilst the leaves were boiled and eaten like spinach and provided an ideal green that was not only rich in vitamins but also corrected dietary over-acidity.

PHYSICAL ASPECTS

A large genus of striking annuals, amaranths vary in height from sixty centimeters to a metre or more. Many have brightly colored flowers and foliage and they often serve as bedding plants for summer color. All species are sold during the spring or summer at most nurseries.

The seeds are also readily available and quite easy to start, providing the soil temperature is warm enough.

MEDICINAL ASPECTS

Medicinally, the orange or red leaves (sometimes green) were once commonly utilized by women to slow down excessive menstruation and made into a decoction that was useful in curing leucorrhoea and other bacterial imbalances of the vagina. Working directly to soothe irritated mucous membranes, it was ideal for treating conditions such as diarrhea and gastroenteritis and to ease the discomfort of stomach or intestinal 'flu and dysentery. The fresh leaves were also applied to battle wounds or other injuries to staunch the flow of blood. A strong tea was brewed and applied in a poultice to reduce the swelling in cases of hemorrhoids and piles.

More recently, this plant's ability to grow in poor soil and a wide variety of climatic conditions has led to its use as a food source in areas tolerated by few other grain crops. In Third World countries, it could provide an excellent dietary supplement for populations that might otherwise starve due to the infertility of their depleted and overworked soil. It is not always an easy task to convert people from their traditional foods to a new and more nutritious fodder, particularly when everything made from the seeds turns out red, but it is slowly being accepted by many people around the world who would otherwise suffer hunger, starvation or malnutrition.

SPIRITUAL ASPECTS

Before the prophesied arrival of Cortez in Mexico on 19 April 1519, an event which coincided with the first day of the Nine Periods of Hell according to the Aztec calendar, the fields of central Mexico were a living carpet of red amaranth. To the Aztecs, she was known as Huauhtli and considered the most sacred of all plants. She provided food, medicine and a reminder of the immortality of all life.

When the Spanish conquered this flourishing culture, the Catholic clergy had all the fields razed and forbade the growing of amaranth. They feared the great spiritual significance that it held for the Aztecs, mistaking such reverence for idolatry. However, their attempts to eradicate it were unsuccessful. The survivors of these once great people kept secret stores of this grain and continued to grow it in small hidden fields awaiting the end of the darkness that was to descend upon them for almost five hundred years.

The life cycle of the amaranth shows why this plant is symbolic of immortality. As with most summer annuals, she commences her life as the soil begins to embrace the warming rays of the sun in spring. Her growth is slow to begin with, but as the pace of life accelerates, she rapidly gains momentum.

Flowers appear at the first sign of heat, and before long she is literally ablaze with color. Even long after death, in the declining months of autumn, she holds up her fiery brilliance and beacons to all those around her, indicating that the termination of those physical functions that we associate with 'being alive' means little to the appearance of the soul. Long after our corporeal bodies have ceased to function, our spiritual bodies shine ever brightly. We can choose to leave behind a legacy of empty husks or we can enrich the world as the amaranth does, supplying the seed of giving to all who will partake.

This is a very protective plant and if planted around the house will help provide security for you and your loved ones. If you place the whole plant in a large medicine bag and wear it over your heart, it is said to protect you not only from the emotional 'slings and arrows' hurled at you by others, but will also provide you with a shield that is literally impervious to bullets or other projectiles.

The seeds of the amaranth, when crushed and ceremonially rubbed on the body, have been known to provide invisibility to those who are pure of heart. The dried flowers, when placed on your prayer altar, will impart a strong sense of immortality to you in your meditations and throughout your day.

California poppy
(Eschscholzia californica)

Sometimes, when I close my eyes on a hot summer's day, sitting still in the brilliant sun, I can see a scene in a place far away and a time long ago, a time when the foothills of California were ablaze annually in a springtime blanket of yellow–orange. As the weather warmed the winter-chilled soil, the rivers were high and abundant with fish, the game was moving up from the valleys and was plentiful, and there were as many California poppy flowers as there were stars in the cool vernal night sky.

The people living in this paradise on Earth were happy and healthy. All were equals and all shared everything. War was rare and seldom fatal, and serious sickness was infrequent. And many of the more common ailments would be treated with California poppy in some form or another.

PHYSICAL ASPECTS

This golden state flower of California exhibits finely divided, deep green foliage crowned by attractive four-petalled flowers in spring. Growing best in sunny, dry environs, it is considered to be a short-lived perennial, occasionally only living for one year in colder climates. Most species set prolific seed and naturalize easily.

MEDICINAL ASPECTS

Salves made from the decocted whole plants were applied to the skin to treat infected or slow-to-heal wounds whilst a tea preparation was used to treat stomach ailments and to quieten colicky babies. The fresh plant was placed on the forehead to ease the pain of headache. In severe cases, the fresh juice of the plant was administered orally. It was also given for stress, an uncommon condition in those carefree spring days before the dying began. A different type of gold was to bring an endless tide of greed and destruction to the land, and like the original inhabitants of this once peaceful place, the California poppy also fell victim to the onslaught of 'progress' and 'development'.

Today there are only relatively isolated pockets of land that still bloom brightly under the California sun, and fewer still are the original people. It is good that many of those who are left are finally being recognized and in some cases given back small portions of their former lands. It is also good to see that California poppies are now being grown around the world in most temperate climates, and that this species is now being seriously investigated for its application as a mild analgesic and sedative, and as an anti-spasmodic.

There seems to be a lot of concern and confusion over the toxicity of all parts of the California poppy. Some say it is poisonous while others consider it relatively harmless. Most, myself included, feel that it is a marvellous herb if used infrequently, with caution, and in the proper doses. This is a plant that I encourage people to grow more than use, unless suitably tutored or qualified. It is definitely not for the novice, and definitely not for those looking for a cheap high. Although it is related to the opium poppy, *Papaver somnifera*, it does not have the same effect and usually just leaves you feeling like dog's breath the next morning.

If you would like to get intoxicated with this plant, I highly recommend planting a handful of seed somewhere where the sun shines the brightest and when they are in bloom, sit amongst the dazzling blooms and dream of a time long ago and a place far away.

SPIRITUAL ASPECTS

If you should one day find yourself sitting in a cluster of California poppies in clear spring sunshine, and you listen very carefully to the etheric sounds that are quietly around all of us but so often drowned out, you may hear faraway voices of spirits that speak about a better way to live. They will show you scenes of a pristine land filled with abundance of every kind, shining in an endless carpet of gold, richer than any mineral dug from the entrails of our Earthmother. Each poppy will sing of a peaceful people living in harmony with the land. They will, if you listen carefully enough, recite the names of those Native American tribes who peopled the land that is now called California, for in every poppy there dwells the spirit of one long departed.

The names will be unfamiliar to you, for they have rarely been portrayed in literature, in movies or on television. Five hundred years of occupation, assimilation, disease and murder have decimated their numbers, but once they were many: the Fernandenos, Chumash, Cahuilla, Wailaki, Modoc, Tatiana, Pomo, Washoe, Yokuts, Salinan and many others.

Now, their spirits have spread out around the world to tell all who will listen that we can once again rejoin the circle that has been broken and bring back the wisdom and ways of these almost forgotten people, to live in peace and harmony in a world filled with flowers. They have come back to herald a new beginning, for the Age of Flowers is here. Now go and plant a seed!

Before you actually go scattering your seeds, there are a few spells and potions that may be of interest to you. I have often found that a sachet of California poppy seeds (it doesn't seem to matter if they come from a seed packet rather than having been collected), when placed under the pillow, will help you attain restful sleep. If you have a question that needs answering, write it on a piece of paper and place it in the sachet as well. The answer will come in your dreams.

One spell that I heard about once but have never personally used is to introduce a drop of the extracted plant juice into the food or drink of someone close to you in order to stimulate 'passion that has cooled'. This is done without that person's knowledge or consent, which is precisely why I would never use it, but it is said to be quite effective.

Poppy seeds are also attractors of love, wealth and fertility, and can be carried in a medicine pouch for this purpose.

Columbine
(*Aquilegia*, many species)

This is one herb that you are unlikely to find in any conventional herb book, and rightly so, for if used incorrectly, it can make you vomit until there is little left of yourself to purge.

PHYSICAL ASPECTS

This hardy perennial grows to about fifty centimeters and produces attractive, lobed dark green leaves and an array of gracefully drooping and spurred flowers ranging in color from white to red and everything in between.

MEDICINAL ASPECTS

All parts of the plant are considered quite toxic and have been known in some cases to cause death. Several hundred years ago, however, columbine was often taken internally to cure diarrhea, jaundice and stomach problems, to speed delivery in childbirth, as a lotion to heal ulcers of the mouth or throat, to ease the pain and inflammation of arthritis and rheumatism, and in homeopathic medicine as a treatment for nervous conditions.

My ancestral Cherokee relations often found it effective in treating heart conditions, whilst the Meskwake Indians added the ripe seed pods (without the seeds) to tobacco mixtures to improve taste and aroma. It was one of the favorite pastimes of Native American children to extract the stamen of the flower by gently pulling on the elongated floral 'spur' until it was released and to savor the sweet drop of nectar produced by the stunning blossom, much as children in our culture once enjoyed honeysuckle.

With a chemical constituency resembling aconite, or monkshood, to which it is related, one might question why this plant was used at all when there were so many other effective herbs to treat the same ailments. There is no simple answer, other than the fact that many factors have changed since it was in common use.

Firstly, it is important to understand that over the last few hundred years our bodies have altered to accommodate our new spiritual awakening and understanding of our place in the universe. Our mental and emotional view of the world has gone through a rapid evolution and with it our bodies have changed as well. Just as new herbs, elements and energies have emerged to help us cope with this change, there are also herbs that once affected us in many positive ways that are now working on the emotional and spiritual levels rather than on the physical.

Secondly, the way in which we heal ourselves has gone through many complex changes, and where it was once considered 'healthful' to regurgitate in order to purge emotional and physical pathogens from within our bodies, one might say that it is now socially unacceptable to cleanse our bodies in this way, although it can often be of great benefit. It is as if vomiting has been given a bad name, for in the old days it was considered a valuable tool in ridding the body of certain toxins or organisms.

SPIRITUAL ASPECTS

Whereas columbine once played a key part in the physical healing practices of the Fourth World it has now strengthened its ability to work on the etheric levels. It has few equals in its ability to help us understand the concept of love that we must embrace if we are fully to enter the Fifth World.

In order to embrace thoroughly real love – that is, the quality of this misunderstood emotion that will heal instead of wound us – it is usually necessary to purge the old concepts that have permeated our minds and culture. We often seek out love as incomplete people in search of our other half, rather than as complete beings attracting, and being attracted by, other complete beings to share in the dance of life.

If we look closely at the flower of the columbine and use a little imagination, we will see how this lovely, multi-hued perennial acquired the botanical name of *Aquilegia*, for *aquila* is Latin for eagle, and it is these great birds that fly closest to the Creator. Love gives us the wings to fly closer to God, and when we learn to love ourselves and others as we are loved by God, then we become masters of the sky. This is why the humble columbine is used so often in love spells, for it radiates this unconditional truth to all those who are willing to learn the lesson.

While sitting close to this plant, imagine how you want to share your love with another person. Do you wish to form a relationship in which you are constantly at each other's sides, seldom straying apart to explore the world around you, or do you want to be like a pair of eagles, each seeking its own space in the sky, free to soar independently through the changing currents of life yet knowing that both will come together again in the shared nest when the day is done? If you want to express your love in the most God-like way, it will be the latter, and once you have experienced it, you will never turn back.

The seeds produced by the columbine are rich in magical properties. It was a common practice of young men long ago to grind up these seeds and apply the resulting paste to the clothing like a cologne. It was believed that by doing so, a person would attract the perfect partner, someone with whom to share a lifetime. If it was used with anything but the purest intent, the result would most likely be, at best, a co-dependent relationship that would serve only as a reflection of the lack of love for the self. Be very careful on this one or you might get exactly what you deserve. This is something I have plenty of experience with.

Another trick I've learned along the way is to rub a few seeds in the palms before shaking hands with anyone that you wish to attract as a friend or a business partner. It is also said that carrying seeds in your pockets, or in a medicine bag, will strengthen your courage and enable you more easily to face your fears.

Eupatorium
(*Eupatorium*, several species)

Whenever I think about this genus of plants I am reminded of the story of Dr Joe Pye and his vision of what had formerly been known as gravelroot (*Eupatorium purpureum*) which cured many people of typhus. There are, however, many other members of this genus – thirty-six in all – growing around the world. Fortunately for you, I will be writing about only three species or we could be here forever.

PHYSICAL ASPECTS

A handsome group of large, hardy perennials often growing to three meters, eupatoriums bear pinkish or purple sprays of flowers in terminal clusters, usually in late summer or autumn. Leaves vary from large and ovate to narrowly divided, depending on species.

MEDICINAL ASPECTS

First, let's take a look at Joe Pye weed, for it is not just a remedy for typhus. As I have said before, this tall, moisture-loving perennial was originally used to relieve people of their gall stones, but it was also given as a kidney cleanser. The root was considered to be an excellent diuretic and was therefore used for many urinary tract problems. Cherokees, and probably most other Indian nations living in the eastern third of what is now the United States, prepared a tea which was given to women in the second and third trimester of pregnancy to build them up for childbirth. Many employed the root to treat gout and rheumatism and as a general tonic. It was also added to a child's bath to help them settle down and get a good night's sleep. The leaves, on the other hand, were applied to burns and taken internally to sweat out a fever.

The second herb, *E. perfoliatum*, is called boneset, even though it has never had anything to do with setting bones. Instead, the flowering tops of this plant were (and in my humble opinion still are) considered to be one of the best herbs for easing the symptoms of influenza. Before the days of 'flu vaccinations, influenza could be a real killer. Almost every herb-wise household would collect quantities of the flowering tops and leaves in autumn to prepare for the coming flu season.

This stately perennial also had the ability to make one perspire profusely and was used to break a fever or treat malaria. It was said to be of some benefit as a tonic, to expel worms from the body and as a stimulant.

To many native peoples it was a panacea and was prepared regularly to treat every imaginable illness, including gonorrhea and snakebites. Many uses of this plant were 'borrowed' from the early European settlers by Native Americans eager to learn new medicines from their white brothers. Many of these practices were derived from the Europeans' experience with their own native species, *E. cannabinum*, commonly known as hemp agrimony. Both names are derived from the plant's resemblance to cannabis and it is this similarity in leaf that has led some poor soul to pull out a few of my young plants from my garden, presumably thinking they would get a high from it. If they survived the experience, they will perhaps be a bit more cautious in the future.

The flowering tops of this towering, shade-loving perennial have been used for centuries to treat a wide variety of conditions, including arthritis, rheumatism and influenza. It has fallen a little out of fashion these days due to its possible association with liver damage in high doses. It is fair to say that all three of these species, if taken in large quantities or for too long, can lead to liver toxicity. However, it has also been used to treat certain liver illnesses. Recently it was found to contain anti-tumor agents and is being investigated for the treatment of some cancers.

SPIRITUAL ASPECTS

Many etheric qualities have been ascribed to many species of *Eupatorium*. The spirit of this plant has the ability to work in many wondrous ways, some of which are being rediscovered and used in love, gambling and securing good fortune in the hunt.

Joe Pye weed has a long history as a love attractor. A piece of the root or leaf can be placed in the mouth before talking to someone that you wish to beguile, as long as they are already in the mood for a relationship. Carrying the dried leaf or root in your medicine bag will help ensure that everyone you talk to will find you attractive and desirable as a friend or companion.

The Potawatomis (I've always loved the name of these eastern Native Americans) used to carry a flowering top of this herb in their pockets when gambling, to increase their winnings, whilst the Cherokee and Seminole utilized the hollow, tube-like stem as a drinking straw. This device was also an important part of administering spiritual healing and one that I have found very useful as well. Whenever any medicine was prepared, this 'blowing tube' was used to impart some of the healer's spiritual essence into the formula. This could be achieved simply by blowing bubbles into the remedy through the blowing tube before it was given to the patient.

After an area of the body had been healed, it was also common practice to spray some protective medicine such as ginseng on the location of the former illness in order to keep it from ever coming back. I don't tend to use this technique very often because people nowadays seem to have an aversion to having a mouthful of anything sprayed on their bodies, but I feel certain that this is a valid and effective tool.

Boneset also has a long history as a hunting talisman, a fibre of the root often being attached to a whistle used to attract deer in the belief that it would sound more attractive to them. It was also believed that if you could slip a small piece of the stalk into the liquor bottle of someone you really didn't like they would soon drink themselves to death.

The spirit of the eupatorium brings you closer to liking yourself, thereby creating an energy that will attract other people to you. She is often called the Queen of the Meadow, and this she most certainly is. She towers over all other perennial meadow inhabitants and has the power to call in almost any other healing or nature spirit. She is a good channel through which to tell your desires, for she will lovingly command many of her subjects to come to your aid.

You may honor her by including any part of her in your medicine bag, pocket or purse.

Licorice
(*Glycyrrhiza*, many species)

Whenever I mention the fact that I grow licorice in my herb garden and utilize it often in many of the medicines I brew up in my home, I get looks of bewilderment followed by some comment about how much the listener loves licorice, and if they had had any idea how good it was for them, they would have eaten a whole lot more of it long ago. Sadly, most people who claim to enjoy the taste of licorice have never actually eaten any of the real stuff, for whoever it was that took the marshmallow root out of marshmallows also took the licorice root out of licorice.

This hardy, spreading perennial has a written history that dates back over four thousand years to the Babylonians, but again I suspect that we have been digging up this plant for food and medicine since well before the invention of the loincloth. The most common species of licorice, *Glycyrrhiza glabra*, originated around southern Europe eastward to Pakistan. Although there

are different species scattered throughout the world, it is the European variety that has become naturalized in most temperate locations. It is widely cultivated for its rootstock and I have seen the taproot plunge into the earth to more than a meter deep.

Until recently I was far more familiar with the American species of licorice, *G. lepidota*, which grows throughout the western states of America. The Dakota people had a wonderful name for it, *Wi-nawizi*, which translates as 'jealous woman', referring to the burr-like seeds which, once attached, are difficult to extricate. Among these people and their neighbors, the root was primarily used to treat childhood fevers, sore throats, diarrhea, upset stomachs, indigestion and coughs. Due to the cooling effect this herb has on the body, it is often still chewed in sweat lodge and during long ceremonial dances. The root was often chewed to relieve toothaches. Many Plains people, who considered their horses to be part of the family, would chew the leaves of this plant until it was a paste then apply it like a poultice to any horse suffering from a sore back.

Now that I'm living in Australia I grow multicultural licorice – that is, Chinese, Russian, European and American species – but find the Russian and European varieties to be the best growers. Each species has slightly different qualities to them, but they are for the most part used similarly.

PHYSICAL ASPECTS

A hardy, rhizomatous perennial with palmate leaves adorning upright stems that produce blue–violet pea-shaped flowers and pea-like seed pods. Licorice spreads, but not aggressively. Species vary in height from forty centimeters to almost two meters.

MEDICINAL ASPECTS

I tend to add licorice tincture to almost every medicine I prepare, not only to improve the palatability of more foul-tasting herbs, but also because it just does me so much good. It is said to be very specific in cases that involve the adrenal glands, due to the fact that one of the constituents is chemically similar to the natural steroids that the body produces.

Being one of those people who tends to overwork during the busy summer months, by autumn I often fall into one big heap if I do not nourish myself, emotionally and physically. My body takes quite a beating, especially my adrenal glands, but I have learned to start my herbal program of regeneration before the symptoms get severe. One of the more important herbs for me is licorice, for it helps to re-balance my adrenal hormones and gets the *Chi* (life force) moving again. I augment this with a program of long, vigorous walks, meditation and a combination of Toltec and Chinese (*Qi gong*) movements that increase the flow of the *Chi*. I also make a vow that I will take better care of myself, with less work and more time for nourishment.

SPIRITUAL ASPECTS

There was a time long, long ago, when children used to receive great quantities of nourishment. They awoke without alarm clocks, often before dawn, and had time to bring themselves gently back from the world of sleep and dreams, listening to the tender sound of the world stirring from the night. On getting up they would engage in play-game aerobics and fill their young bodies with nourishing oxygen and adrenalin. Before schools were invented to keep children busy while their parents went to work, the young ones would spend the rest of the day exploring or learning a skill from some 'grandmother' or 'grandfather', an elder who might or might not have even been related.

All adults were responsible for all children – not only in nourishing, but occasionally in punishing. And when a child got a special treat from friend or family, it was not only mouth-wateringly sweet, it was often good for them. Even 'candy' was nourishing. There were angelica stalks coated with sugar, marshmallow root filled with herbal goodness, apples covered with anything impossibly sticky and chewy, popped corn held together with maple syrup and plenty of licorice roots to chew on.

Now we see children cramming their bodies with every imaginable sort of modern day confectionery, filled with artificial flavors, coloring and texturing and with enough preservatives to keep the snack fresh long after the child has reached adulthood. It saturates them with empty calories and throws their young adrenal cortex into chaos. Blood sugar rises and falls like a roller coaster and the price of the ride is malnutrition, exhaustion and depression.

The spirit of licorice beckons us back to a time of nourishment, for if we do not receive enough of it for long enough, we suffer terrible consequences. If we give our children or ourselves too much stress and not enough nutrition, the adrenal gland can actually shrivel up and quit working. Licorice teaches that it is now time to return to the pursuit of happiness, good nutritional balance and nourishment of ourselves (all four levels) and our families, neighborhood, community and the world.

The roots of the licorice tell the story. If you look closely you will see many small nodules dotting the roots. These nodules contain nitrogen which has been absorbed by the plant in a process called nitrogen fixing. Licorice and all other plants in the legume family are able to provide their own nourishment in this way. When a young licorice plant begins this process she first feeds herself (the self) so she may grow. When she has grown, she starts constructing a taproot (the family), and when this is strong and deep she begins sending her nutritious rhizomes out in every direction (the community). She is not invasive and nourishes those she grows close to (the world).

The seed, like an idea whose time has come, will stick to you if you brush against her and will in turn stick to anyone else who comes close enough to you to share your seed, figuratively and literally.

If you wish people to be more attracted to you, it might be wise to place a few licorice seeds or burrs inside your medicine bag or pouch. These are said to attract love, friends and sex – all very nourishing things.

If you are like I am and have trouble nourishing yourself, I would suggest either taking licorice in whatever form you choose, providing you are not hypertensive, or carrying a piece of the root somewhere on your body. A small taproot can be drilled and worn around the neck as a reminder to you to nourish yourself at every chance you get. Bracelets can be fashioned out of the runners that spread from the plant and worn in times of stress.

A licorice stick can be decorated with beads, stones, feathers or whatever you have that contains 'value' and be made into a healing wand. If you are really craving a cigarette, try sucking on a licorice root instead. This does two things that a cigarette cannot do: make you healthy and make you passionate.

Lobelia
(*Lobelia*, many species)

There are a great many species within the genus of *Lobelia*, but one in particular, *L. inflata*, has probably gained the most attention over the years. This plant was known for centuries by the native people of America as a herb that was extremely useful in the treatment of croup, asthma and bronchial spasms. It was given freely to the early colonialists who in turn documented its effectiveness and brought this knowledge to the rest of the world. Native Americans so revered this herb for its medicinal and magical properties that the seed was often transported great distances by medicine men and cultivated near their encampments to ensure a readily available supply throughout the year. It was one of the few plants cultivated by the Pawnee and Crow people of the Great Plains area of America.

PHYSICAL ASPECTS

This is a variable genus consisting of over 350 species worldwide. Some lobelias, like *L. inflata* (Indian tobacco), are annuals, whilst most other medicinal species are hardy perennials. Many species, such as *L. cardinalis* (the cardinal flower) and *L. syphilitica* (the greater lobelia), have spectacular blooms in summer and autumn.

MEDICINAL ASPECTS

Although this herb has been known to cause death if taken in large doses, when administered correctly it has long been considered indispensable in the treatment of asthma and other upper respiratory ailments.

The leaves and flowers were most often smoked in a medicine pipe in order to get the ingredients directly to the source of the problem. For this reason it was commonly called Indian tobacco, even though it was never used as a substitute for the real thing. In fact, it was often smoked to cure people of habitual tobacco smoking, and I must say that having a few puffs of this plant is likely to keep anyone from ever wanting to smoke anything again.

When ingested orally, it often produced vomiting, which in most Indian cultures was considered a good thing. In fact, it was often used just for this purpose as a remedy for poisoning and in the practice of ceremonially

inducing regurgitation to cleanse the mind and body before any important council meeting. This was a fairly common practice amongst Native Americans, and one that is still employed today, although much more rarely. This is why it has earned several other common names such as puke weed, emetic weed and gagroot.

At one time it was common practice among the Cherokees and many other Eastern tribes to treat syphilis with another species, *L. syphilitica*, commonly called greater lobelia. There is still a debate about whether this disease was brought back to Europe by the first explorers of the Americas or whether it was already there before 1492. It was certainly present in the Amerindian population in pre-Columbian times, but no one is sure exactly when it came to Europe.

My guess is that it was probably brought back to Europe during some earlier exploration of America, possibly by the Vikings or some other band of randy European voyagers whom we are presently unaware of. According to most of my Native American sources, there were many visitors to Turtle Island (one of the Indian names for North America) in pre-Columbian times, all of whom presumably had sexual contact with the native people.

While the cure seemed to work quite well for Amerindians, it was eventually deemed ineffective by the European medical establishment. Whether this was due to genetic differences or the fact that it was always used in conjunction with other herbs is a matter of conjecture. Either way, I do not recommend using it for this purpose.

The root of this plant was also taken as a tea for treating many other complaints, including breast cancer, scrofula, diarrhea and dropsy, whilst in powder form it was applied externally to skin ulcers, wounds and inflammations.

A third species, *L. cardinalis*, commonly known as the cardinal flower, was also used for many of the same ailments treated with greater lobelia, although it is said to be more effective in treating bronchial spasms and invaluable as an expectorant. It has been said to be a strong sedative plant. However, great care must be taken with this and all other species of *Lobelia* or you might find yourself sedated right out of this lifetime.

SPIRITUAL ASPECTS

The phrase that keeps going through my mind when I am in communication with the deva, or soul spirit of this plant, is that she is here to 'calm the tempests that we manifest into our lives'. She can quiet the emotional storms that we create through our inability to bring healthy love into our circle; she can calm the emotional factors that produce violent bouts of coughing in our bodies and she will help us to see how we may better love ourselves so as to live our lives more completely, if not to the fullest, and express our love in a healthy God-like way that mirrors the way that God loves us.

Many forms of coughing may be caused by misdirected or conditional forms of love. Illnesses such as bronchitis, asthma and croup are often a result of repressed anger over the issue of love, and can only truly be healed when these matters are brought to the surface and dealt with in a positive and responsible way.

If you cannot give love as it is truly meant to be given, it is difficult to receive love. For those who see love relationships as a constant battle, a storm moving all around with little respite, a lack of love and respect for the self are probably the cause. When we redress this imbalance we suddenly find that there is more than enough love to go around. The more you give, the more you receive.

If you are ready to make the transition to a higher level of love and esteem for self and others, *Lobelia* will guide you through this major shift. She will open up gateways of perception that will frighten yet enlighten you. It is never easy to view and examine our own shortcomings, but it is a necessary step in our development towards living a spiritual life. It can be painful, but you will reap the benefits of your work through the love that you attract.

The brilliant red flowers of the cardinal lobelia (*L. cardinalis*) and the rich, vibrant blue flowers of the greater lobelia are some of the best meditative mediums I have used to deal with this problem. They can be placed on your prayer altar either fresh or dried as a reminder of the inner work you wish to achieve. During meditation you can call on the plant deva to bring you visions of where and when the problems began, and how best to deal with them on all four levels.

Another method is to place some of the dried foliage of *L. inflata* and flowers of Indian tobacco into a prayer pipe and smoke it, taking care not to inhale. When you exhale, let the smoke be the medium through which your prayers pass from your lips and enter the realm of Spirit. This, too, can bring you visions concerning the cause and effect of the problems you have given yourself in this life to resolve. If you don't like the idea of smoking, it can be just as effective to scatter the dried plant as an offering to the Creator, Earthmother and the Adawees, or guardians of the four directions that help create our physical reality. If you choose, you may simply meditate next to any of the lobelias and ask them for guidance. If you are quiet and patient enough, she will help you with your struggle.

Wearing a medicine bag containing the dried foliage and flowers will help as a daily reminder of the journey you have embarked on.

Anyone who thinks that couples never fought in the old days will be disappointed to find out that they were, in that regard, no different from anyone else. They still had some of the same struggles in marriage that face us today. Separations and divorce were not all that uncommon, and it was normal for couples to quarrel and fight. However, the Amerindians, at least, had one thing that we lack in our Western culture, and that was magic. The most successful spell used to bring quarrelsome couples together involved a third party secretly 'spiking' their food with very small amounts of grated lobelia root (not poisonous in such small quantities). After eating a few meals together with this magic in place, the couple would once again return to marital bliss.

Finally, if you are planning an outdoor activity or having a barbecue and are concerned that an approaching storm will ruin the occasion, try casting some of the herb to the wind and asking for the storm to abate. With any luck, you might just get the desired result, even if you live in Melbourne or Tasmania.

Sweetgrass
(Hierochloe odorata)

Now we come to the final entry on our herbal Grandmothers, and it is indeed a case of saving the best till last. Actually, it just worked out that way alphabetically and organizationally, but it is appropriate that we finish this section off with her, since she represents the epitome of Grandmotherly energy.

Sweetgrass was and still is a fundamental component of the many sacred ceremonies, purification rites and healings in which Native Americans participate (as all human beings should).

PHYSICAL ASPECTS

A hardy spreading grass with deep green leaves which, when grown in damp conditions, will reach over a meter in height.

MEDICINAL ASPECTS

Sweetgrass has served medicinally to staunch excess blood flow after childbirth, and to help expel the afterbirth as well. The tea made from the leaf has also been employed to treat coughs, colds and fevers, but moderation is required due to the presence of coumarin, a toxic substance. It is coumarin that imparts the delightful fragrance associated with sweetgrass but which, in large or frequent doses, has been shown to cause liver damage and hemorrhages.

I believe a lot more meditation and research needs to be done on this plant to find out what valuable medicine she has to offer us amidst changing medical perceptions of the twenty-first century.

My hunch is that someone will find a startling new use for this rather ordinary looking grass and she may end up saving many lives.

SPIRITUAL ASPECTS

The dried leaves of this moisture-loving perennial grass are most commonly braided and burned to release the cleansing smoke. The technique used is similar to the burning of sagebrush, except that, instead of driving out negative influences, it acts to bring in good and benevolent spiritual forces. In essence, it is like attracting ethereal moths to a bright flame.

Wachanga, as she is called by the Dakota people, who we often refer to collectively as 'the Sioux', was often called on to draw in these good energies before and during almost every ceremony and council. Any time people were meeting to discuss war, peace or any other important decision, sweetgrass would signal the spiritual elders to come forth and impart their infinite wisdom to the proceedings in order to make judgements that were based on Godly principles rather than through ego, retribution or individual beliefs. Smudging with sweetgrass would always set the proper and respectful atmosphere needed to deal with the conflicts that would inevitably come up in any family, community or cultural circle, as well as securing a spiritual blessing on any new endeavor.

It is good to see many of these practices still set firmly in Native American gatherings today. There seems to be a great revival taking place throughout America, in Indian as well as non-Indian people, for this is not just a custom that is reserved for only one race or culture.

Indeed, sweetgrass has its roots sunk deeply in many peoples of the world. In Europe, it has also been an important part of the spiritual practices of the Celts, as well as many other early tribal people, and utilized in much the same way. Even in New Zealand the Maori people gathered a very similar species of sweetgrass to sanctify any spiritual practice. This is another example of the synchronicity the binds us all together as human beings and brings the world collectively closer.

As a perfume, sweetgrass has few parallels. Rubbed on the body or plaited in the hair it has an aroma unlike any other, although to me it sometimes has the faintest hint of cinnamon while at other times it triggers lingering olfactory memories that I can never quite identify. Maybe it's like the smell of new-mown spring grass with a touch of vanilla. More often it reminds me of a place I've heard about where you can learn the lessons of life without pain and suffering. A place where we can lie down beside the still waters and be overwhelmed by the beauty, the tranquillity and the sweet scent of grass heating up in the warmth of the sun.

When we call in the 'wisdom of the elders' through the use of sweetgrass, it is important that we be as free as possible from any mental, emotional or spiritual pollution, for it is these spirit beings that seem to bring out any hidden flaws in our character and shove them directly in our faces.

Many people would like to believe that, by calling in 'good spirits', their lives will be washed clean of any negative feelings that may lie deep in the psyche, but this is only wishful thinking. If, in our life's journey, there is work to be done that we have not faced up to yet, these spirits will make sure that it is lovingly brought out in the open to be dealt with. There is nowhere to hide from these pure beings, and until we front up to the 'monsters of the id', our lives can get pretty confronting.

There is no magic wand that we can wave that will wash away our 'sins'; only hard work and a real yearning to become more spiritual beings within the physical world.

We must be ready to accept responsibility for the words and

actions that we bring the world before being allowed to sit with this spiritual council of elders.

I prayed for many years to be allowed to grow sweetgrass here in Australia. Each time my prayers were answered, but the answer was always 'no'. After many years of trying to find or collect some seeds, only two years ago I was finally sent the seed to start growing my own supply of this plant, and I have only just started to be able to receive the harvest from my hard work.

These things take time, and for some the wait is long but rewarding.

PART 4

the grandfathers

Seven sacred trees

Ash

(Fraxinus, many species*)*

There would be few neighborhoods in Australia that would be without at least one ash tree, yet most of us consider this esteemed tree to be little more than a beautiful ornamental plant, useful only for shade and appearance.

The truth is that, in times past, the leaves, wood and bark often played an important role in the physical and spiritual well-being of a great many people throughout the temperate regions of the world. This rugged relative of the privet, lilac and olive, which is not to be confused with the 'environmental weed', the mountain ash (*Sorbus acuparia*), is not the type of tree that jumps out at you. It has not the beautiful flowers, striking bark or delicious fruit that mark some of its cousins, yet for those of us who are willing to stop and listen, it speaks volumes.

On the practical side of things the wood of this humble tree has been used for making an incredible array of items, including snow-shoes, tennis racquets and boat oars. For the common people of yes-teryear it also provided the ideal material for the making of a wide variety of kitchen utensils due to its smooth, pliable, splinter-free nature. On both sides of the Atlantic ash trees were commonly made into bows and arrows and I've heard that the wood was preferred by Native Americans for making spears. The Ojibwa nation of the Great Lakes area of America and Canada has recorded a multitude of virtues bestowed on the local Black Ash (*F. nigra*), which has pro-vided material for the construction of canoes, the covering of the wigwam (their circular living abode), pipe stems and tool handles.

It is interesting to note that, in both America and Europe, the wood was once considered a valuable tool in keeping snakes away and curing the effects of snake bites. Staffs or walking sticks were used to repel snakes while walking in their habitat, at least in the Northern Hemisphere, where these were said to clear the path of rattlesnakes. In Australia it's probably always a good idea to carry some sort of staff while walking, if only to have something to put between you and an advancing snake. It is said that snakes will do anything to avoid crossing ash wood, making it a rather popular protective barrier for those camped in rattlesnake country. I'm told that many people still believe that you can heal a snake bite simply by tying a circle of ash twigs around the neck of the victim. I prefer a compression bandage and a good dose of anti-venom, myself.

PHYSICAL ASPECTS

Most ash trees grow anywhere from ten to twenty meters, with a few species growing shrub-like. Although some of the ashes bear male and female flowers on separate trees, most contain flowers of both sexes. These are followed by an abundance of winged seeds which can travel a great distance.

The ash is a remarkably resilient and adaptable tree. There are species that will grow fairly quickly in most temperate to semi-tropical areas, making them an ideal shade tree for gardens and in street plantings. They have few problems with pests and disease.

I enjoy this tree not only for its symmetry of growth and lack of litter (the sometimes messy fruit of some species notwithstanding), which makes it ideal for the Virgo in me, but also for the way sunlight filters gently through the summer foliage. Several species, such as *F. velutina 'Modesto'* (yellow) and *F. osycarpa 'Raywood'* (reddish purple), exhibit a spectacular autumn blaze of color.

Most ash trees will grow in just about any soil type, depending on species. Some are well suited to desert conditions, whilst others prefer to have wet feet in winter. They tend to be relatively drought resistant, although almost all species enjoy a good deep soak from time to time. They require little fertilizer and will also tolerate being grown in a lawn situation. All do best in the full sun but will tolerate growing in the shade of a tall canopy of gums.

MEDICINAL ASPECTS

Medicinally, the sap, leaves and bark have been employed for a wide variety of ailments. Amongst the Cherokee people the bark was decocted into a tea that was used for stopping an excessive menstrual flow, while the inner bark was made into a tonic for stomach and liver complaints. The Iroquois had a habit of kicking off (not cutting or scraping) the root bark to make into a poultice for snake bites. I don't know why this was considered the only way to collect the bark, except that maybe they just felt like 'kicking ash'!

The sap of at least one species (*F. excelsior*) is still used as a gentle laxative that is particularly effective in treating the very young, the very old and the very pregnant. A favorite cure for earache was made by burning the middle of an ash stem until the sap began flowing out of the cut ends. It was then allowed to drip into the affected ear.

The seed has a reputation for being somewhat of an aphrodisiac and was (and maybe still is) used to stimulate lustful feelings in men, and increase sperm production. The seed is also said to make urination easier for some.

In Russia, China and Manchuria the leaves and bark have been utilized to stimulate blood circulation in the extremities, which would have been particularly useful in their long, cold winters.

The bark tea is still a traditional medicine of many Native American people for afflictions such as eczema, head lice, sore eyes and flatulence, and as a wash for women after childbirth.

SPIRITUAL ASPECTS

The ash tree is a powerful protector of human beings, offering shelter not only from serpents but also many other forces such as lightning. I have seen tipis with an ash branch affixed to the top of one of the poles to ward off lightning strikes, while many original cultures in Europe believed that this attracted lightning. You make up your own mind, but don't blame me if you're wrong!

It is of very little doubt that the wood of the ash tree has the ability to ward off certain spells and negative influences. Carrying a piece of it, particularly a twig that has been blown off the tree, in your medicine bag will protect you against such things and provide you with the ability to transform emotional energy into spiritual energy. A staff hung over your doorway will help keep out any emotional vampires. In an emergency you may use it to prod them out the door. A cross fashioned from equal lengths of wood will protect you from drowning in the ocean, just as it shelters us from drowning in a sea of emotion.

My father, blind and barely ambulatory in the last years of his long life, made a daily ritual of walking out to the Modesto ash that he planted in the backyard and caressing its bark, talking silently to it in a language that only he and the tree knew. I always felt that he was tapping into the energy given off by the deva and that this helped him detach from the emotional aspect of life, helped him move more fully into the spiritual and aligned him with a sense of well-being, for that is the gift of this tree.

As we observe its physical form we see how cleanly and straight it grows and how perfectly formed the crown is. Imagine the earth energy travelling through your body and upon reaching your crown chakra radiating equally out into the universe. This aspect of the ash was recognized by the ancient Teutons, who honored it as the Tree of Life.

If you sit under an ash tree or use its medicine, think about how we may utilize the power of the plant to help protect us from the highly energized world of today and find growth and tranquillity in almost any environment.

The leaves, if placed in your pocket, may be used to attract a lover. I had a friend who used to fill a sock with ash leaves and stuff it down the front of his pants before going out to a dance, but I doubt that this had anything to do with magic.

The best use for the leaves would probably be to sew them into a sleep pillow, which is said to promote psychic dreams in which your higher self can better see those loves that will benefit you and help you to be nourished.

Many people believe that it was *F. ornus* that provided Moses and the Israelites with manna in the form of exuded sap during their exodus, which is how this tree derived its common name, manna ash. As it fed the bodies of these oppressed people, let it also sustain our souls with life-giving nourishment.

Cedar
(*Thuja species* and *Calocedrus decurrens*)

The term cedar is a generic term, rather than a botanical one, for a large group of evergreen trees that includes not only true cedars (*Cedrus* sp.), such as the cedar of Lebanon and the Atlas cedar, but can also refer to several genera of trees such as *Thuja* (white and western red cedar) and *Calocedrus* (known as incense cedar and red cedar), which is not a cedar at all but a species of juniper.

To make things even more confusing, there is a native Australian genus of trees also called white cedars (*Melia*) that is not even remotely related to the true cedar, but instead belongs to the Mahogany family. In this section, we will ignore botanical nomenclature and deal with trees which, from now on, I will call by their common names. They are the incense cedar (*C. decurrens*), the eastern white cedar (*T. occidentalis*) and western red cedar (*T. plicata*).

The incense cedar is a large evergreen tree that lives in the mountains of California, southern Oregon and Nevada. It derives its name from the fact that the Amerindians used it as an incense. Like other plants that are used for smudging, it was highly revered by the people who shared the same geographical range. It is a very fragrant tree, particularly in warmer weather, which is why the branches were often scattered on the floors of sweat lodges and in homes to 'freshen the air' – both physically and spiritually.

The Washoe people who occupied Yosemite Valley built large tipi-like structures called *umachas* for storing their supply of acorns. After erecting the framework from lodge-pole pines, strips of cedar bark were put in place to serve as the walls and were lined with worm-wood to keep out the insects that would otherwise ruin the harvest.

Due to the rot-resistant qualities of the timber the trees were often used in the construction of homes or long-houses. The wood of the western red cedar is still used extensively as an outer cladding for many modern homes around the world.

The eastern white and western red cedars have many common properties and can be used interchangeably, so, rather than differen-tiate between the two, I will call them both cedar.

These cedars are also evergreen conifers and can grow to enor-mous size, particularly the western species, *T. plicata*, which can attain a height of over sixty meters. You may not recognize it, but the variegated form of this tree is very commonly grown in Australia as an ornamental plant and often pruned to form a hedge. It is rare to find a suburban street that doesn't have at least one of these trees in the yard, although they often look more like bushy shrubs.

In case it's not obvious, the eastern white cedar grows through-out the colder regions of eastern America and Canada, whilst the western red cedar occupies a broad area from California all the way north to Alaska. Once again there are no true species of cedar grow-ing in the Americas and we only call them that to confuse people. Many people living in the east call their indigenous 'cedar' by the name *Arborvitae*, which means 'tree of life'.

Now that you are all probably baffled, I will say that both species have been used as smudge plants and are used as such to bring in good spirits, much like sweetgrass.

The incense cedar is a large evergreen tree that lives in the mountains of California, southern Oregon and Nevada. It derives its name from the fact that the Amerindians used it as an incense. Like other plants that are used for smudging, it was highly revered by the people who shared the same geographical range.

PHYSICAL ASPECTS

The term cedar often refers to several different species of evergreen conifer. Most, although classified as trees, are useful as hedges if regularly pruned. They have dark green, fan-like foliage and rough, reddish bark. There are several variegated species.

MEDICINAL ASPECTS

Medicinally, both cedars share most of the same attributes and were most often brewed into a tea to relieve headaches, colds and coughs and to ease some forms of rheumatism.

As with many other conifers the foliage was traditionally added to boiling water and the steam inhaled to clear blocked sinuses and relieve other kinds of respiratory congestion.

The branches were once slapped across the body of those partaking in sweat lodge purification, much as Scandinavians to this day use whips of foliage to stimulate the skin and increase blood circulation. The fragrant foliage of both was also laid on the floor of the sweat lodge to purify the area – both physically and spiritually – as well as being bundled into smudge sticks for smoldering. The smoke, besides purifying, was occasionally employed to revive comatose patients.

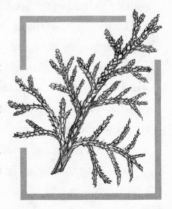

Most Native Americans practiced birth control but were not above drinking a strong infusion of the leaves to promote termination in cases of unwanted pregnancy. This brew also served to promote menstruation.

The leaves, prepared as a poultice, served to reduce swollen hands and feet. The young twigs of the *Arborvitae* are still used today in herbal medicine to treat bronchial congestion and improve muscular tone within the urinary tract to aid in cases of incontinence. Externally, the sap is said to reduce or eliminate warts.

SPIRITUAL ASPECTS

People throughout the world consider the cedar to be the 'tree of life'. It is a tree that connects us to the higher forces that are all around us, and brings us together as human beings.

It is not uncommon to see branches of cedar being waved through the air during many purification ceremonies conducted by the native people of the American north-west, particularly when consecrating a new home or during weddings and other auspicious occasions.

The smoke, as I have mentioned before, is used primarily to bring in good energy or spirits. The foliage is often mixed with other smudging plants such as sagebrush in order to 'chase out the bad and bring in the good'. Cedar smoke is an ideal medium in which to send your prayers to the Creator.

Hanging a cedar bough outside your exterior doors will help ensure that only good influences come through while negative ones are kept out. It is also said to be effective in warding off lightning strikes. Golfers would probably benefit from carrying a short polished staff of this wood to afford them some protection against electrocution during storms, although it would still be prudent to suspend the game and head for the pro shop.

I was once told by an Iroquois friend that in order to rid yourself of the memory of a nightmare, you can whittle a small branch of a cedar tree into the form of a little knife and scrape your tongue with the edge of it upon waking from the bad dream.

Liquidambar
(Liquidambar styraciflua)

This is one of those trees that many people love to hate. But love him you must, for the resin that is extruded from this handsome, deciduous tree is still an ingredient in many soft drinks and is still used in medicines for its antiseptic qualities, and as an excellent expectorant. In 1926 it was listed as American storax on the official United States Pharmacopoeia, where it is still listed to this day.

You may know this tree as sweetgum, a name that refers to the gum that oozes from the trunk or branches when they are injured. It has often been planted in Australia in suburban yards that are far too small to accommodate its spreading root system, and this can destroy pipes, footpaths and planting space. Every Saturday or Sunday morning in leafy suburbs you can hear the sound of lawn mowers hitting the surface roots, which is much harder on the lawn mower than it is on the tree.

You can also hear the obscenities being hurled when someone in bare feet steps on one of the spiky round seed cases that litter the ground from late summer till winter. When planted in an appropriate location, however, the liquidambar has few parallels for durability, medicinal qualities and vivid autumn coloring. Every tree is a living picture on which is painted bright yellows, oranges, reds and deep purple.

So valued was the sap, referred to as copal or storax, that it was often traded by tribes living amongst these picturesque trees to people living far from its natural range. When Cortez met with the Aztec ruler Montezuma in 1519, he was introduced to cigarettes that had been soaked with this fragrant gum and to the notion of burning it as incense and applying it warm to the cheeks to relieve a toothache.

PHYSICAL ASPECTS

A fast growing deciduous tree reaching to over twenty meters, the liquidambar is covered in glossy, palmate leaves which turn a brilliant scarlet color in the autumn and winter. Inconspicuous flowers produce spiny balls which drop in spring. The bark is attractively furrowed.

MEDICINAL ASPECTS

The gum has had dozens of uses. It was once used to treat diarrhea and herpes sores, and (as a dressing) to draw out any infection from wounds and skin ulcers. Early explorers suffering from allergic skin reactions were cared for by the Cherokees, who applied a salve made from this substance as a cure.

Native Americans probably learned of its value by watching wounded animals rub their injured parts on sweetgum trees that were weeping sap. It was also enlisted to reduce fevers and treat dysentery as well as for tuberculosis and asthma.

The gum was collected much like syrup from the maple tree, with an incision being made into the bark and the extract later being scraped off and stored for future use. When hardened, it was chewed like chewing gum and was said to be most beneficial to dental health.

The bark was also gathered and most often boiled to make a tea for frayed nerves.

SPIRITUAL ASPECTS

Take the time some day when the sun is shining its autumn light on Melbourne's Dandenong Ranges, or on any hillside or even a small corner of nature where the trees have put on their dazzling autumn robes, to make yourself good and comfortable, and rest your soul and your eyes on the spectacle that unfolds in each liquidambar leaf as it readies itself to end its cycle of life and provide the forest floor with the future of lives yet to unfold. Many colors bleed together in these leaves, creating what must be one of the great visual wonders of the world. I cannot imagine what life would be like without the autumn show of oaks, poplars, planes, elders, ashes and, best of all, the maples and liquidambars.

In Gembrook, where I live, as throughout the rest of the Dandenongs, the hills are alive with explosions of color. Near my home there is a driveway that is planted on both sides with sweetgums. I pass by that driveway nearly every day on my walk into town, and at the time of writing this book it is very difficult to keep myself from stopping and admiring the view.

Most of the time I succumb to the energy of these trees and make myself comfortable for at least a few moments just to soak it all in. As I look with all three eyes I am transfixed at what I see and feel. Looking down this long, sweetgum-lined drive that disappears over the hill, a certain melancholy begins to fill my heart, for I know that it will be many cold months before I once again can energize in the heat of the summer sun. Everything around me is withdrawing its energy, except perhaps those plants that relish these cool, rainy moons and make the best of it while they can.

For me, through the vibrational qualities of the sweetgum, it is time to reflect over the past year and evaluate how much my will has grown. Was it a year forward, standing still or regressing? Was my will strong enough to conquer and rule over desires and compulsions, or did it cave in and just go with the flow?

The spirit of the sweetgum teaches us about using our wills to manifest all that we can. We all have a certain task to do here on the Earthly plane, but without the will it may not get done. Many of us go through life knowing we are here for a purpose but find ourselves locked into our old programming and not having the will to release ourselves. This is a common trait amongst us two-leggeds and it is hard to break free.

The sweetgum tree can help us understand just how powerful the will is. With his own will, he can split asunder even the most heavily laid concrete because his will is constant and unyielding. When one is doing the Creator's will, nothing can permanently block the way. The more one chops away at the root of the sweetgum, the more numerous the suckers he sends up to dull and defeat even the toughest lawn mower.

The spiny 'fruit' of the liquidambar are equally unscathed by encounters with mowers, often shooting back at the person doing the cutting. If we dare hold one of these in our hand we learn another lesson. The fruit represent life and are appropriately called prickle-balls, for that is what life often is. We cannot dig into the fruit to fetch the seed without seriously injuring ourselves, so we must wait and hold the proverbial balls by the prickles until the seed is ready to be released. This takes willpower. When we learn just when to use our will to wait and when to use our will to go forward, we learn one of the secrets of life. Without will, we are nothing but circulating thought patterns waiting for the end. The will is all about NOW.

Oak
(*Quercus*, many species)

An oak tree, like many of the trees I have described in this book, is hardly the type of plant that one would think of seeing at a herb nursery, yet there it could well be. Maybe you think I'm trying to stretch things just a bit, but the truth is that even though it has somewhat limited applications in the medicinal sense, it is one of those trees that has an ancient, time-forgotten bond with human beings that makes it difficult to dismiss. It calls us back to a time when magic was an entwined part of medicine, and healing was facilitated on all levels.

Of course, to most people inhabiting the once vast oak forests
of Europe and America, the most
valuable commodity supplied by
the oak tree was the acorn. If you
have ever taken a taste of this large,
protein-filled 'nut', you may well
wonder how this extremely bitter
and unpleasant tasting food source
was ever considered edible.

Several means were employed to rid the acorn of its acrid taste;
however, the most effective method was demonstrated to me by an
elder of the Washoe people (the Num), who lived peacefully
amongst the great stands of oak and pine that dominated the western slopes of the Sierra Nevada mountains of California. A small
quantity of acorns, generally enough to make a week's supply of
food, was removed from the *umacha* or storage building and, once
extracted from the shells, would be ground on the granite rocks,
sifted through baskets, and reground until reduced to a fine flour.
This flour was then either placed in a hole dug in the sand next to a
stream or put in a finely woven basket and 'leached' by repeatedly
pouring water over it until most of the bitterness had been rinsed
away. The resulting dough was then removed and either baked into
bread or, if it contained much sand, was placed in waterproof baskets
and made into soup or gruel by adding water, then heated by placing
hot rocks into the liquid until it boiled. This technique often took all
day, but with all the women working together it became more of a
social gathering than a chore. I have heard that, in many native
tongues, there was only one word for both work and play.

PHYSICAL ASPECTS

Oaks are usually large, spreading, deciduous or evergreen trees with
thick leathery dark green leaves variable in shape from holly like to

extremely palmate. The distinctive acorn is produced through the summer and generally drops in autumn. The bark of many species is deeply furrowed. Catkins of cream to yellowish flowers appear in spring.

MEDICINAL ASPECTS

The most important physical property of the oak tree is the high tannin content found in the bark and leaves – up to twenty per cent. This makes it very useful, when made into a salve or ointment, as an antiseptic for burns and wounds and highly beneficial in reducing infections, particularly those occurring in the orifices of our bodies that are rich in mucous membranes. Tannin can also help to form a protective layer over the tissue within the intestinal tract, making it valuable against some forms of diarrhea.

The same ointment was used by native people in many parts of the world for treating vaginal infections such as leucorrhoea and in soothing sore eyes. I know that several eastern tribes used a decoction of the inner bark to help bring up phlegm from deep within congested lungs. The Cherokee used tea made from the bark and rubbed it over their skin to comfort dry, chapped derma. The same brew was used to tan hides.

SPIRITUAL ASPECTS

In many cultures, oak trees were revered for their great age, wisdom and strength. To the Druids, who were considered by the Celtic people to be spiritual healers and keepers of the sacred truths, the oak tree was an indispensable part of every sacred gathering. When women paid homage to the nature spirits and danced naked in the moonlight, it was always in the presence of an oak tree. It was their guardian and protector, valued more than almost any other tree. Branches were often fashioned into staffs and walking sticks and were said to protect the carrier from any harm. The wood was also carved into objects that were used to call in benevolent spirits and the acorns were said to be an attractor of everything from money to good health.

Native Americans also had a wide variety of spells and spiritual beliefs associated with the oak tree. One love spell that I recall involves the making of a cigarette from tobacco and dried oak leaves. This would be lit and smoked. Every time the smoker exhaled, he or she would utter the name of someone they would like to have a relationship with, blowing the smoke in the general direction of the person they were trying to attract. This was done four times, then the smoker would bury the rest of the cigarette. It was also believed that touching an oak tree whose branches intertwined with another oak tree would ease the pain of loneliness.

Oak trees are great communicators. If one oak is attacked by leaf-eating insects such as caterpillars, it will not only begin increasing its content of tannin to ward off the attack, it will also signal other oak trees in the neighborhood to warn them of the possibility of an impending assault so that they, too, can increase their tannin content.

Through meditation and communication with the great oaks, we learn the importance of measuring spiritual growth not in years but in the strength that it brings us. It may take an oak tree fifty years to produce offspring, but to the oak time is meaningless. They live in true abundance, for they share their bounty with many. Abundance is only worth something if it is shared with all.

There was a time in my life when I believed that making any sizeable amount of money was not a good thing. I had seen so many people who were rich but lived selfish lives and I mistakenly thought that money always corrupted the spirit. I swore I would never fall into that trap, and constantly ran away from opportunities to make financial gains. I lived in what I now call poverty consciousness.

Then, one day a few years ago, I was visiting friends in Yosemite, my old mountain home of long ago, and while sitting beside a stream that wound through a beautiful, lush meadow in all its early summer glory, I was approached by an ancient elder whom I knew to be an excellent basket maker, one of the few left who still practiced the old ways.

Without introduction she sat beside me and pointed at two oaks nearby. One was in the middle of the meadow and because of its prime location, with plenty of earth and nutrients to sink its roots into, was healthy and loaded with acorns. Birds, insects and animals of every description were making use of his shelter and food, and their lives were abundant and happy. The other tree lived just outside the meadow, in the rocky talus of the valley walls. You could easily see that this tree had little in the way of fertile soil and in the winter months lived in the shadow of the rock faces that surrounded the meadow. Many times he had been hit by falling rocks and avalanches of snow and ice. His limbs were only sparingly adorned with leaves, and produced little if any food for the other creatures.

My basket weaving mentor then asked me which tree I would prefer to be, and of course I pointed to the patriarchal one in the meadow. To that, she simply said, 'Then why have you chosen to live your life like that poor malnourished tree growing in the rocks?' In an instant that changed my life and outlook forever. I knew what she meant. Abundance is a very godly thing so long as it is shared and not hoarded from all those in need. I do not seek monetary gain for any selfish purpose, but only to help provide those who are in need with food, shelter and the strength to go on.

Pine

(Pinus, many species*)*

I'm afraid I may be a little biased here, having come to Australia from a landscape covered with many species of pine and other conifers. There are days during the heat of summer when I wish I could lie down and rest on a carpet of pine needles and take deep draughts of the air as it rises from the odiferous cushion that the pine has thoughtfully dropped. Fortunately for me, and unfortu-

nately for the Australian environ-
ment, there are many areas in Mel-
bourne's Dandenong Ranges that
are host to several varieties of pine,
planted there years ago to supply
wood for the mills and now gone
feral. Luckily for the environment,
and unfortunately for me, there is
now a large scale effort to eradicate
these invading trees, which I support, except for the fact that I will
have to go back to America to get my olfactory thrills.

There are several species of pine that produce great quantities of
edible nuts, such as the Scots, pinyon and stone pines. Actually,
most pine trees produce nuts that you might say are edible but
hardly palatable.

Most people think of tipis when they think of Native Americans,
even though only a very small percentage of Amerindians utilized
this unique structure. For the ones who did, there was one species
of pine that was prized above all others, and that was the lodge-pole
pine, *P. murrayana*. They often travelled great distances to obtain
the strong, straight poles that supported the tipi, or traded with
people living closer to a supply.

PHYSICAL ASPECTS

This huge group of evergreen coniferous trees has needle-like leaves
in bundles, and bears those familiar pine cones. Although best
known as tall upright species, they vary in height from five meters to
over fifty meters and often have interesting contorted shapes.

MEDICINAL ASPECTS

Medicinal applications of the pine tree were many and had nothing
to do with whether or not you lived in a tipi. The Cherokee people,
who lived in rectangular, timber-framed houses, had a long list of

ceremonial and medicinal uses for this stately conifer. Most often, the sticky resin was boiled in water and the cooled liquid applied to swollen testicles or breasts. This syrup was considered safe enough to treat coughs and colds contracted by pregnant women. A tea from the needles was given to flatulent ball players (ball games were very popular with the Cherokee, but flatulence wasn't), and instead of throwing away the boiled needles, these would often be applied to the forehead to cure headaches.

Pine tar, which was generally extracted by boiling the roots and skimming off the lighter resins, was considered an excellent substance to smear on for relieving 'the itch', probably some type of skin rash like crotch rot that so many early explorers were susceptible to. It was also applied to rheumatic joints and festering wounds, and used as an all-purpose ointment when mixed with pig fat. Pine tar graced medicine cabinets throughout America for over a hundred years before being replaced by more modern antiseptics, and now has been relegated to the kitchen as a lowly floor cleaner.

Modern herbalists still use the needles and buds of several species of pine in the treatment of upper respiratory problems and some forms of bronchitis and asthma.

SPIRITUAL ASPECTS

There are 1022 spells, magical formulas and supernatural beliefs from the many cultures around the world that recognize the pine tree as a powerful spiritual entity. (Actually, I've never counted, but there's lots.) These majestic trees are the mystics of old that have come back, forever to look upwards in silent worship of God.

In many Native American circles, it is the common pine needle that is considered the preferred smudging material. I use it quite often and find it very cleansing and beneficial to the soul. In water-cleansing ceremonies, a green pine needle cluster which has been blown from a tree can be used to sprinkle water onto the subject's body. Pine boughs are often brought inside to cast out bad spirits and flies. It is also little known that a fall from even the tallest pine tree will never kill you. Of course, the landing might.

To most lay people, any tree that is evergreen and has needles and cones is a pine tree. On closer inspection, and armed with a bit of botanical knowledge, one begins to see the subtle differences between pines and other species in the Pinacea family. I suppose the lesson here is that somewhere along the way we have become so distant and far removed from the natural world that we often fail to take the time really to *see* it. Most of us can see the world around us, but we have lost the art of *seeing*. This is the word that the spirit of the pine refers to when radiating the message about the difference between looking and *seeing*. This tree, which has a worldwide distribution, can see it all. Each species communicates with his coniferous brothers around the globe, and each tree has the true ability to *see*. We can learn from them how to see once again as children see.

Do you remember a time when you used to see creatures of every description in the ever-changing canvas of the clouds? On the other hand, remember when you were a child and you were frightened because, in your room at night, you saw a monster that turned out, with the lights turned on, to be only a pile of clothes or a shadow cast by your robe hanging from the wardrobe door. This is the time that the spirit of the pine can bring us back to, so we can turn on the light and learn to *see*. Practice sitting or lying under a pine tree and ask for the gift of sight. Really look at things, examine them, study them, feel them with your eyes. If there are clouds in the sky, imagine.

Senna
(Cassia, many species*)*

When deciding on the herbs that I was to write about in this book, there was certainly no lack of plants to choose from. Much of the problem lay in allowing my mind to relinquish control and let the Spirit do the work, not an easy task for a reforming control addict such as myself. The name *senna* kept popping up, so I knew I would have to add it to my list of herbs. I'm glad I did because, ever since, I have been feeling the presence of a long departed relative of mine whose name was Senna Bear. Although I never knew her, I can *see* her, and know that somehow she has reached out across a century and more to help me complete this project. There were times when I felt I could go no further and was ready to chuck the whole thing in. At these times I could feel her urging me to release control and let the power of the universe guide me.

This is the energetic quality of senna, and at times it can be quite aggravating. Just as physically irritating qualities force the bowels to expel their load, so it is in the etheric realm.

PHYSICAL ASPECTS

Sennas are showy herbaceous perennials, some evergreen and some deciduous. These woody shrubs and trees have
attractive finely cut pinnate leaves and
bear pea-shaped yellow flowers in spring
and summer. Some species bloom year
around in warmer climates and most
produce interesting seed pods.

MEDICINAL ASPECTS

No matter where you travel in this temperate world of ours, you are likely, should the need for a good laxative arise, to encounter the healing qualities of senna, for it grows almost everywhere. Whether you go to Asia, Africa, North or South America, Europe, Australia or India, you will find at least one species that will do the job. Generally, it is the leaves and green seed pods that are used for this purpose.

The Cherokees made a tea from the leaves to treat intestinal cramps caused by constipation, but more commonly it was the root that elicited the most attention as a poultice for skin ulcers and as a tea for heart troubles, to renew and invigorate tired sportspeople on the field, and to reduce fever in children.

For the black slaves recently abducted and taken to a country that had little in common with their African homeland, it must have been at least a small comfort to find the American senna (*Cassia marilandica*) growing throughout the countryside and providing the same medicinal qualities that they had known from indigenous African species, among them *C. didymobotrya* or *C. nairobensis*, to name a few.

The Chinese, who call their native species *Jue ming-zi* (*Cassia tora*), have learned many ways of utilizing this plant. Besides being a valuable treatment for constipation it is also said to soothe tired, bloodshot eyes, improve vision through the cleansing action it exerts on the liver, and reduce high blood pressure. The seed produced by the stunning yellow flower clusters served as a remedy for sore throats among many Native American people living in the eastern third of America, and is made into a food seasoning in some countries. In larger, nearly toxic, doses it was taken to expel intestinal worms.

The laxative action of senna comes from its ability to dehydrate, thereby irritating the lower tract and facilitating 'evacuation', a nice way of saying bowel movement. It is still commonly found in many over-the-counter commercial medicines.

SPIRITUAL ASPECTS

Spiritual constipation is a result of people trying to control that which should pass through our lives, but gets blocked by fear. It can be looked at in two ways. Firstly, constipation can be the manifestation of someone who receives enough nutrition from the world but then holds onto it instead of allowing it to exit, for fear that later they may not get enough. It is a form of poverty consciousness: a fear that, even though there is nourishment now, it may not always be there. The second cause can be when we are constantly faced with people feeding us emotional crap that we are unable to pass on or recycle. Some people are very good at just passing the crap along in an endless chain of scat (that's the unscientific way of saying feces), whilst others retain every last bit of it and become emotionally and physically constipated themselves.

Working with senna helps re-balance the process that we use to absorb what is needed for personal growth, and eliminate that which is unnecessary waste product. This plant helps us off-load what qualifies as emotional surplus or excess baggage, and in doing so frees up the balance of give and take. We often take aboard way more than we deserve, and this eventually becomes quite toxic. The challenge is to take on only what serves to fill our emotional stomach and to recognize the rest for what it is: excrement. Loving yourself and others is the key to knowing which is which.

You can tune in to this energy simply by carrying senna seeds in your medicine bag, or in your pocket. The seed of many species is said to remain viable for well over a hundred years, so when you have worked out the reasons for your spiritual, emotional and physical constipation, make a small notch in each seed coat and plant them in a warm, sunny location for further generations to find.

If you wish to attract unconditional love from someone in particular, try getting a senna seed and placing it on the ground where the other person is likely to walk. When you are sure they have stepped on the seed, plant it in any appropriate location. If it grows, you will find this love mutually.

Witch hazel
(Hamamelis virginiana)

For many years I assumed, gazing at the ancient bottle of witch hazel that lived permanently in our bathroom medicine chest, that whatever was in that container was very powerful medicine, since it was obviously made, or at least used, by witches. That bottle was older than I was, maybe older than my parents, and as far as I knew nobody in the house had ever had call to use it. I assumed that it was only for real emergencies, like if you cut your hand off or something.

As I grew older and was able to read the oil-stained label, I was rather disappointed to find out that, for the most part, it was used only as an antiseptic, as after shave lotion and in treating mild sprains, bruises and 'muscular discomfort'. I was further disenchanted as a young horticulturalist to find out that the witch in witch hazel referred not to women stirring cauldrons but to an Anglo-Saxon word which means 'to bend', alluding to the excellent bending quality of the wood of this plant, which was often used to make bows.

If there are any plants living on Earth that were originally from another planet, this could be one of them. Although said by botanists to be related to the liquidambar, it bears little resemblance. It produces eerie yellowish flowers that look more like an undersea anemone, or one of those weird starfish that they find at the bottom of some oceanic trough. They also have the unusual habit of blooming in autumn or early winter, often just when last year's seed capsules begin audibly to snap open, sending the seeds flying in all directions. Wherever this smallish tree originated, it was always considered invaluable bush medicine to the people inhabiting its relatively confined habitat of eastern North America, with a few related species in eastern Asia.

PHYSICAL ASPECTS

A small deciduous tree with unusually shaped yellow flowers in autumn or early winter. Witch hazel grows to about eight meters with somewhat straggly looking branches and oval-shaped leaves which turn yellow–orange in autumn.

MEDICINAL ASPECTS

The Cherokee found the bark tea useful for washing skin abrasions and bathing wounds as well as for easing painful menstruation and as a gargle for sore throats and mouth ulcers. All Native people played sports, and some of these games were unbelievably rough. Broken bones, cracked skulls and internal injuries were not uncommon, but it was all in good fun. Before and during each game the participants would take time out to massage in liberal quantities of witch hazel. This kept wounds clean and eased tired, battered and aching muscles. It was also used by women as a douche for yeast infections and internal hemorrhaging.

Many Amerindians brought the twigs and leaves into the sweat lodge to help open up and cleanse the pores of the skin while loosening up tight muscles. When made into a tea the leaves were said to be superb for curing hemorrhoids and piles, and when diluted this brew was employed as an eye wash for relieving the inflammation.

After nearly falling into obscurity, like that old bottle that one day disappeared from our bathroom apothecary, witch hazel is fortunately being re-introduced to our modern medicine cabinets. May it live there long and prosper.

SPIRITUAL ASPECTS

Many will say that the world we have co-created is filled with mental abrasions, emotional contusions and spiritual wounds. If we ignore a wound, or simply apply a Band-Aid, hoping it will heal itself, we may find later in life that these injuries will begin to fester, becoming inflamed and infected. This is the importance of dealing with life's hurts as they happen, making sure we look closely at the damage and if necessary cleaning them out well, even if it means digging deep to excise every last bit of dirt and grit to make sure that they heal over properly. It usually hurts to do this, just as it is painful to pour witch hazel onto a tender cut or raw flesh, but this discomfort is needed to keep the injury from giving us trouble as we progress through life.

We are all given the instruments we need to facilitate this process, but often leave them on the back shelf of our medicine cabinet, much as my magical bottle was left to age and eventually be discarded. We do this because we are too afraid to re-open the wound and flush out the infection, or we simply forget that the injury ever existed until it begins throbbing with pain as we get older.

The modern world provides us with a myriad of Band-Aids to cope with these battle scars. The most widely utilized is television, which can certainly deaden the pain, but does nothing to actually heal us. The list can include sex, which can be used to distract rather than attract, constantly going out to 'have a good time' at the club or hotel, drugs including cigarettes and alcohol, sleeping pills, tranquilizers and anti-depressants. Let me stress here that I consider the last three to be important medical tools – over-used perhaps, but vital to many people who otherwise would not be functional. However, if we do not look at these difficult times as an opportunity to re-open our wounds and clean out the mess that lies beneath, then we are doomed to suffer again and again.

Witch hazel is symbolic of one of the more positive and long-lasting aspects of the healing process. We must dust off the bottle of this elixir and apply it liberally, through techniques such as counselling, anger management, hypnotherapy, introspection, massage, prayer and meditation (which I believe are pretty close to being the same thing), and a myriad of other tools that have been given us from all parts of the world to help us through these difficult times.

In order to move more fully into the Fifth World, it is now necessary for all of us to grit our teeth and begin experiencing the pain that we try so hard to forget. We can help each other as extended families or tribes, all healing each other and being healed in a united effort to make life a less painful experience. There will always be injuries to the mind, body and spirit, but if we take the time to be able to probe deeply within our own souls and clean them out, we may find that there is, underneath the scab of denial, a treasure trove of understanding and acceptance to be found.

Witch hazel can be added to massage oil to facilitate healing on a deeper level. Often we develop blockages throughout the energy field that exists within us, and these can be manifested as aches and pains that respond well to massage and a healing touch. It may open memories that will give us clues as to the nature of our injury.

The wood of this lovely deciduous tree can inspire us to go deep into our pain and re-live the moment to get a clearer picture of what we need to do to heal. This wood can be made into healing staffs and wands and held as we meditate or just sit in a peaceful spot to reflect. The green leaves can be rubbed onto the body as a sort of green smudge to cleanse us from our pain and anger whilst the seeds, if you can find them, are very beneficial when carried on your person.

If you are lucky enough to have a plant nearby, try sitting close to it and receive the healing energy that this plant gives off. One of the tasks given to Cherokee priests (men and women) in their training was to sit amongst the witch hazel plants in autumn and listen to the seed pods catapult their seeds to the four directions. Each time a capsule would release its load, the initiate would be required to bring up something that had caused them pain. In this way it was shown that, out of this suffering, would come the seeds of under-standing that would sprout and bring forth new life and energy.

Seven sacred shrubs

Aloe

(Aloe vera, many species*)*

I know that many people would argue that this succulent plant doesn't really belong in the shrub section of the Grandfather plants. Technically, aloes come from a broad class of plants that have adapted well to heat and drought and are called succulents. This is the type of plant where you just have to throw away terms that become meaningless, for they don't fit our traditional way of judging what is a tree, shrub or perennial. I basically had nowhere else to put it, so here it is as the first entry of the seven sacred shrubs.

When I was a young boy growing up in Southern California, I had a great love for nature, inheriting my grandfather's appreciation for plants, but had never had much to do with herbs or their usage. One day I came home from school to find a strange-looking succulent plant growing in a clay pot on our front porch. The label had been hand-written and simply said, 'Aloe vera, African burn plant. Rub sap of leaves on burns to relieve pain.' My mother had no idea who had left it there, but decided to put it on the kitchen window sill and look after it. It was probably the first house plant we ever grew, and it was a good choice, for it seemed nearly indestructible and grew well.

PHYSICAL ASPECTS

A very common and popular succulent plant with rosettes of spiny-toothed, sword-shaped leaves, generally light green and mottled in appearance. Many species of aloe have showy, tubular flowers. They reproduce mainly through underground shoots near the base of the parent plant.

MEDICINAL ASPECTS

Being somewhat accident prone, I had occasion before long to use it when I burned myself on a very hot pan. Remembering the label, I decided to give it a try, and to my great surprise the pain subsided within minutes. I had rarely used anything that didn't come from a bottle or tin, and it was a revelation to me that a plant could actually have such a profound effect.

I became probably the world's leading young proponent of the use of this plant, telling anyone who would listen of the marvellous healing qualities contained in its plump foliage. Better still, the original plant began sending out offshoots which were quite easy to pull off and transplant into new pots, enabling me to give away my new discovery to many friends and neighbors. I will always remember that aloe vera and its many descendants (some of which still reside on the very same windowsill) – not only as the first herb I ever worked with, but also as the first plant I ever vegetatively reproduced.

Now I know that aloes are not just for burns, and have a wide variety of healing attributes. Coming originally from South Africa, with many other species worldwide, the plant spread quickly, and so did word of its miraculous abilities. It was known to the Egyptians and those living around the Mediterranean area before the birth of Christ, and, in fact, was apparently used to anoint the body of Jesus before he was buried in the tomb.

The use of this plant spread through Europe over a thousand years ago and was brought to the Caribbean and South America by the Spanish about four hundred years ago, when it was planted as a commercial crop. In recent years it has been grown on every continent except Antarctica, unless someone there is growing it as a house plant over their kitchen sink!

Over the centuries aloe vera has been utilized for many purposes, most notably as an ingredient in almost every skin care product in existence. It is even advertised on television, which means that it has reached superstar status amongst herbs and humans. It is commonly employed to coax suppressed menstruation and in treating liver conditions and jaundice. It is also a uterine stimulant, which makes it unwise to use internally during pregnancy; and, due to its strong purgative effect, should also be avoided by nursing mothers as it is easily passed on through the milk.

Aloe vera can also be used as a laxative, although it is best to abstain if you suffer from hemorrhoids. It has been credited with healing abraded skin, bites and stings of all sorts, acne, asthma and even arthritis. As with all medicines, though, it is important to remember that some things work better for one person without having much effect on another.

If you are one of those people who are mildly 'herbophobic', aloe vera is the one for you. Even if you never use it for anything but sunburn or kitchen accidents, it is well worth giving it a try. Look what it did for me.

SPIRITUAL ASPECTS

Not only was aloe vera the first herb I ever grew and used, it has also been a totem, or guiding spirit, for me. Put simply, a totem is a spirit or etheric entity that guides us through the many hurdles we face if we wish to develop as human beings. Many people consider this rather far-fetched at best and sacrilegious at worst, but it is neither. Whatever you may choose to believe, it is worth investigating the spirit that I believe is a part of the life force of the aloe; with patience and an opened mind, you can feel it too.

Aloe is a strong protector but, because he works in such a gentle, caring and nurturing way, his energy is often mistaken for feminine. Let's just say that aloe is masculine with a very strong feminine side – a sort of a SNAG (sensitive new age guy) amongst his contemporaries.

When you grow an aloe vera in your house, it will add life and abundance to the environment. Whenever I use lotions or creams on my body, which is often, I like to give thanks to the plant in my house for helping to ease the wrinkles of sadness and hardship from my physical body and anointing my soul with nourishment and love. I think about how we humans have the ability to transport such a living thing on our travels to discover the world, and now, other worlds. How clever we are to be able to do such a thing, and how clever of aloe to tempt us with his healing life-blood to establish him in almost every corner of the Earth.

When I was in South America, I noticed that every household had a large aloe plant hung upside-down by the doorway. I was told that this was to keep away any malevolent spirits, and although I don't adhere to the custom, I'm sure it works. These people tend to be orthodox Catholics and don't see any problem in blending ancient traditional folklore with conventional religion, finding that, if anything, it enhances both practices.

Meditation, particularly the Golden Pathway technique, should connect you with the spiritual essence of the aloe. You will feel protected and cared for, as though someone strong was massaging your face with gentle fingers. He will ease your furrowed brow and life-burnt skin, and will even make you feel a little younger.

Cascara sagrada
(Rhamnus purshiana)

Although there are many species of *Rhamnus* growing throughout Eurasia, North Africa and North America, the one I have chosen here is *Rhamnus purshiana*: cascara sagrada, or sacred bark, which grows exclusively in the Pacific north-west from Northern California all the way up to British Columbia.

PHYSICAL ASPECTS

This is genus of large, fast-growing shrubs, sometimes small trees. Some species of cascara are deciduous, whilst others maintain their oval to elliptical leaves year around. Attractive smooth reddish bark and berry-like fruit make it appealing in the garden. The flowers are rather small and rather insignificant.

MEDICINAL ASPECTS

Also occasionally called buckthorn, particularly when referring to native species on the east coast of America and Europe, most species produce a bark which, when dried, is amongst the best medicines ever administered for constipation. While the use of many species seems to have gone out of fashion, cascara (I call him by his first name) has a very different effect from that of some other plants, such as our friend cassia, in that it has a gentle action which moves things along without being irritating about the whole matter.

Cascara is often a prime ingredient in many commercial preparations for constipation. At one time, vast stands of cascara and other *Rhamnus* species were all but eliminated in order to corner the bowel movement market at the turn of the century, when people were so anal retentive. Substitutions were commonplace and demand for the real cascara made prices extraordinarily high until commercial growing began to increase the availability of this fine medicine.

The fact that the bark must be dried for a few years or subjected to a special drying process always makes it in demand. A tea from the bark has been said to be useful in reducing certain forms of rheumatism and some Native Americans made a poultice, by either chewing or boiling it, and applied it to difficult wounds and inflammations.

Personally, I would save my bark for someone who would really like a gentle and safe way to lose a few ugly pounds through using this laxative.

SPIRITUAL ASPECTS

To know cascara sagrada is to know the peace of the cool, damp forests of the Pacific north-west. It is a place where one gets dwarfed by the towering fir trees that dominate all but the chainsaw, a place where you can look deep inside yourself and begin to let go of the stress that keeps you bound up inside.

The drumbeat of the native people can still be heard reflecting this almost somber environment in slow rhythmic percussion and low, muffled song and chant. It is a land of great beauty and intro-spection that I have felt in a few other places in Australia – for example, the Dandenongs and Cape Otway, and I have heard that these can also be found in Tasmania.

The feeling is dark and clouded in mist – not menacing or sad, but rather the quiet joy of one who has gone deep inside and come out with the shining light of knowledge. If you can find a bit of cascara bark, hold onto it during your meditation or prayer and feel the energy going up your arms and into your shoulders. From there it will radiate through the rest of your body, settling in on the base chakra. There it will resonate with the note we know as G. You can hear it if you listen with your heart.

All species of *Rhamnus* seem to play a major role in breaking hexes and fighting against the forces of darkness, regardless of where it is grown in the world. The bark is an excellent material to put in a medicine bag or pouch. When you feel tense or angry, hold the medicine and take yourself back to the cathedral of the forests. There you will find what you are looking for.

The bark of the cascara bush was once scattered around an area that was used by Amerindians as a 'courtroom'. All legal matters that faced the individual or the society were discussed in an open, honest way where everyone had the right to voice an opinion. The scattering of the bark was to assure that justice and right action would be done. It could be worth a try in our court system!

Creosote

(Larrea tridentata)

When I was a young boy my family took a trip to the Sierra Nevada mountains of California and, while there, visited what was at that time the oldest living thing in the world: a giant Sequoia (*Sequoia-dendron giganteum*) said to be over 3,000 years old. I could not then, nor can I now, comprehend how anything could survive on Earth for so many years, but there it was, showing us the way back to when Moses was in diapers.

By the time I was in high school, the most ancient being was a bristlecone pine, *Pinus aristata*, which had been core-sampled at an astounding 4,600 years old. These gnarled and weathered trees have survived in an area of the Sierras that hosts one of the harshest climates and highest altitudes in the mountains. At over three kilometers in elevation, these trees germinated at roughly the same time as our Western 'civilization' did in Mesopotamia.

I only just got used to that concept when it was announced that someone had carbon-dated a creosote bush, *Larrea tridentata*, at around 13,000 years. The seed for this plant might have been part of the flotsam and jetsam of the Great Flood, which I believe happened at about that time, and may well have been one of the first land plants to begin re-colonizing the flooded Earth. I have often wanted to visit that ancient being, but commonsense has persuaded the discoverers not to disclose the location of this relic for fear that it would be vandalized. I have, however, visited many other creosote bushes in the search for medicine and wisdom.

On the physical level, these plants have provided the desert-dwelling inhabitants of the south-west with centuries of healing and purification. Creosote is actually a misnomer since the bush contains none of the substance known as creosote, a commonly used wood preservative derived from coal tar, although a tea made from the leaves and twigs does taste like creosote smells.

PHYSICAL ASPECTS

This extremely drought resistant American shrub has aromatic, leathery two-part leaves and yellow flowers borne in spring followed by downy seed cases. The leaves go from light to dark green, depending on availability of water. Creosote grows to about three meters, with equal spread.

MEDICINAL ASPECTS

The leaves of creosote plants, also called chaparral, were once used to treat diarrhea and stomach difficulties. They were also applied externally, as well as ingested, for the relief of rheumatism and minor aches and bruises. Creosote was more importantly known as an anti-tumor agent – thought to be useful in shrinking active malignant growths – and indeed there seems to be some scientific evidence that it may be effective in many forms of these devastating cancers.

The plant contains several anti-bacterial and possibly anti-cancer agents that are also highly efficient at scavenging those nasty old free-radicals that age and corrupt our bodies. The Native Americans knew nothing about anti-oxidants or free-radicals but often took it as a 'body cleanser'. However, they were wise enough not to take it for extended periods due to its possible toxicity to the liver.

Many tribes applied the chewed leaves to bites and stings of all descriptions and boiled up the branches to treat the symptoms of influenza. The Paiute and Shoshone treated serious burns with a similar decoction mixed with animal fat, whilst the Pima found it useful in relieving abdominal pain, cramps and dysentery. I have even heard of chaparral leaves being rubbed on the body as a deodorant, although I can't understand why anyone would trade their body odor with that of an old telephone pole. Whatever gets you through the day, I guess!

SPIRITUAL ASPECTS

What would it be like to live for nearly 13,000 years, to see the coming and going of great civilizations, to survive the cavalcade of life riding the roller coaster of climatic and environmental changes, and to witness the countless genera of creations unfold and then return back to the mud of evolution?

We learn by observing or partaking in this ageless herb, incorporating those aspects of energy we need in order to rid our lives of those things that make us so transient on our journey through life. Human beings have the capacity to live far longer and in far greater health than we do, and in a much richer and fuller social environment than we have co-created.

By examining the physical qualities that chaparral exhibits, we can bring the lesson into our own lives and community to make this the world it was meant to be.

If we look at the growth pattern of the chaparral, we see that it starts out the first hundred years of its life growing into a rather scraggly, rounded shrub about one metre tall and about twice that in spread. As it leaves its infancy, the original growth at the center begins to die off and decompose very slowly and the plant continues to grow outward. After a few hundred years or so it has died off enough in the center to have the appearance of a large powdered doughnut. This continues on for thousands of years until the diameter of the shrub measures some nine meters.

Little grows inside the diameter of these ancient bushes due to the fact that the roots secrete a germination inhibitor that prevents other plants from getting established. It is only when heavy rains leach this substance out that other wildflowers can begin growing within the confines of the chaparral, but when the inhibitor begins to re-accumulate in drier weather, everything dies off again.

In our lives, as we grow ever outwards like the chaparral, everything that is no longer needed for survival dies and decomposes into the Earth, for this is the way of life. If we hang onto things for too long, they stop serving a purpose and just add to the extra weight of our existence.

Every negative thought or emotion is like a weed seed trying to germinate within the core of our lives, and if we do not discard the hardened leaves of the past, we cannot protect ourselves from the physical, emotional, mental and spiritual weeds that will sprout from our life's perimeter and eventually overpower us. We must try to inhibit these thoughts and emotions that attempt to age and destroy us, and regularly take stock of those weeds that have germinated within our minds, freeing ourselves from the burden of having others and their actions feed on us from within. A small piece of chaparral root in your medicine bag will be a constant reminder to you to keep your life weed free.

Internally, we can manifest catastrophic illness and greatly accelerate our ageing process through our thought patterns, for every negative thought or action is brought into our lives as a free-radical, a toxic by-product of life that builds up over time to break down our cellular functions. Free-radicals can be destroyed through a powerful anti-oxidant called nordihydroquaiaretic acid, or NDGA, which is present in chaparral and several other plants. Just as this constituent decreases the number of free-radicals in our physical body, so the spirit of the chaparral does this for the soul. He helps us to search out the positive in every action and event so we do not pollute our mind, body and spirit with those free-radicals that are born in anger, disappointment and negative thoughts from the past.

The fuzzy seeds of the chaparral are delightful to handle, for you are touching something that has survived countless generations of change and extremes only to be made stronger and more enduring. Place a few seeds on your prayer altar and reflect at each meditation on the potential for everlasting life.

Juniper

(Juniperus, many species*)*

Rarely does one find a herb that is so widely used, in such synchronistic fashion throughout the world, as the juniper, for it is found in the medical lore of virtually every country where it grows. This covers a lot of ground, for there are well over sixty species of this evergreen shrub or, occasionally, tree. It has spread over all continents except Antarctica; and I would suspect that, in time, when that territory thaws, even it will probably host several species as well.

If I ever get abducted by aliens and they allow me to take just one species of plant with me to an otherwise desolate planet, I will probably choose juniper, for it has the power to supply food, warmth, shelter, medicine and spiritual solidarity. If I could smuggle a few rye seeds in my pockets, I would even be able to make bread and gin. This is why the juniper is yet another plant that some people still consider to be a 'Tree of Life'. It is said to be associated with thunder and everyone knows that Thunderbirds (the mystical birds that bring thunder; not the TV show) live in a forest of juniper.

In my pre-computer file of index cards I have filled over four pages with notes on the many uses of juniper, but I should be selective. Did you know, for instance, that shredded juniper bark often served as diapers for Amerindian infants and in stuffing their cradle mattresses?

PHYSICAL ASPECTS

A large genus of evergreens ranging from trees to trailing shrubs, all possessing needle- or scale-like leaves and often bearing round fruit. The color of the foliage can vary from dark green to golden depending on species.

MEDICINAL ASPECTS

On the medicinal side of things it would probably be easier to tell you the illnesses that juniper has *not* been used to cure, or maybe I could just start at the top of the body and work my way down. This versatile herb has been used for hair growth, headaches, failing eyesight, stuffy sinuses, blocked noses, loose teeth, tooth pain, sore throats, aching muscles, breathing difficulties, irregular heartbeat, stomach gas, kidney stones, liver tonic, internal hemorrhaging, urinary infections, obstructions within the uterus, constipation, and a number of skin conditions and ailments.

For the sake of brevity, it might just be enough to say that I have found the berries to be very useful in improving digestion, as a diuretic and antiseptic in treating urinary tract infections, and as a laxative which also reduces flatulence. I do not recommend the use of juniper during pregnancy or for those suffering from certain kidney complaints.

Junipers come in a wide variety of shapes and sizes. There are ground covers, such as *Juniperus horizontalis* and *J. chinensis* 'Sargentii', shrub forms like *J. chinensis* 'Pfitzerana' and 'Armstrongii', and many columnar shapes, as with *J. chinensis* 'Columnaris' and *J. communis* 'Stricta'. There are even several tree types, the best of which is, in my decidedly biased opinion, the pencil pine, *J. virginiana*.

SPIRITUAL ASPECTS

Juniper is one of those plants with which I have always had somewhat of an affinity – that certain closeness that one has with a kindred spirit or with a long lost brother found after a lifetime of separation. I need not be anywhere near this tough and hardy shrub (or tree) to tap into his energy, and each time I get a crystalline picture of his appearance and nature, as often happens when we begin to develop a good relationship with our totem plants. In physical terms, I see him as a kind of spiritual 'mountain man' type – not very tall in stature but very heavily built and solid as a granite boulder. He is covered in a thick, seemingly impenetrable coat of deceptively spiny-looking but very soft foliage which covers him from head to toe, except for his face, and even this is hidden under a thick beard made up of long needle-like 'hairs'.

The most striking feature is the eyes, which shine out from behind the shag rug face with purple–blue orbs of light that penetrate my very soul. He reminds me of some old stereotypic trapper, ageless yet ancient in his knowing of the difficulties of life and compassionate of our journey, for he has been there too. He has lived amongst the remorseless craggy peaks that provide so little shelter from the cold, howling winds of winter and has survived the worst this world has to offer. His strength has come from endlessly facing the challenges that God has to offer and gaining fortitude and resilience in the process. He has survived famine, drought and icy winds only to become stronger and wiser, and will share this erudition with all who have the commitment and fortitude to face the blizzardy elements of life.

Following the spiritual path – 'the good red road', as it is often called – is never easy. Many people believe that, if you live in a righteous way, the journey will become smooth, but this is rarely the case. When you make the conscious decision to put behind you all those things that keep you out of touch with God, you may find your trail becomes harder and steeper. This is not a punishment from Spirit but rather a necessary acknowledgment of the resolution we have accepted to change our lives.

The spirit of the juniper helps us, through example, to be strong and resilient when confronted with the winter storms of our learning, knowing that the bright springtime of understanding is just around the corner, and the summer warmth of knowledge and illumination will follow.

The foliage of junipers, particularly the pencil pine, *J. virginiana*, was often used by the native people of the eastern third of

America for smudging. Its purifying smoke is said to cleanse away any negative energies. Performing regular smudging ceremonies will help strengthen and fortify you during difficult times. Placing a few of the scale-like leaves in a medicine bag will help you hurdle any spiritual obstacles placed in your way.

The wood of the juniper is said to be a strong protector and will ward off any negativity that is sent your way. It can deflect this energy back to its point of origin. The berries can be carried by men to bolster their 'masculine qualities', if that is what they want.

A staff made from a juniper branch can guard you against snakebites and provide an etheric shield against the malevolent forces of others.

Manzanita
(Arctostaphylos uva-ursi and others*)*

One of the common names for this particular species of evergreen shrub is kinnikinnik, which can be confusing when you read that Native Americans often smoked 'kinnikinnik' in their pipes. The term can mean almost any smoking mixture, whether it has kin-nikinnik leaves added or not. In other words, it is possible to smoke kinnikinnik without actually smoking any kinnikinnik. It is a generic term which simply means 'smoking mixture', but for the sake of clarity, I will call the plant manzanita, which is Spanish for 'little apple'; or bear berry, a reference to the fruit, which was relished by bears and many other animals, including the human kind.

Some species of manzanita are more upright than *Arctostaphylos uva-ursi*, which is considered a ground cover. *A. manzanita* and *A. glauca* are just a few of the forty-three species growing throughout the dry areas of western America, mainly California. They are typi-fied by strikingly smooth wood (when not peeling) which is often reddish in color and leathery, light green leaves and hanging heath-like flowers followed by green berries turning orange or red in autumn.

The wood was once considered to be sacred and was used in the construction of homes and for sweat lodge ceremonies. To the California Amerindians, such as the Chumas, Fernandenos, Chilula and others who have only just re-emerged from the brink of extinction, the wood was fashioned into pipe stems. The process was long and laborious as it had first to be drilled down the center (it is a very hard wood), then soaked in boiling water so that it would not crack while drying. Then it would be given a good coating of bear or eel grease and left standing until the wood had completely dried out and absorbed the grease. Finally, it was attached to the bowl, often made of soapstone, antler or clay, using juniper pitch for glue. Of course, the most popular smoking agent was tobacco and kinnikinnik.

The fruit was traditionally eaten raw, dried for winter, cooked or scorched and made into a gruel or porridge. It was also ground into powder for making cakes. The fresh or dried fruit can be made into a lovely cider by crushing them and adding them to just-boiled water. When cooled, the brew is poured through a 'sieve' of pine needles to filter out the big bits. The fruit can also be made into jam or jelly and is said to stave off scurvy.

PHYSICAL ASPECTS

Evergreen shrubs with leathery light grey to dark green, often oval or lanceolate leaves and nodding waxy pinkish flowers followed by fruit that resembles miniature apples. The bark of the crooked stems and trunk is usually reddish and quite smooth.

MEDICINAL ASPECTS

Traditionally the leaves were mashed into a paste and applied as a poultice to open sores or wounds and also laid on the forehead and temples for headache. For sore and aching backs the Cheyenne would make a decoction of the leaves to be taken internally whilst the healer massaged the liquid into the affected area. The same brew was used to alleviate heavy menstruation; it was always taken in small doses to keep the medicine from irritating the small intestine.

Traditional uses of this herb – for clearing urinary tract infections or 'gravel', and in treating water retention and inflamed kidneys – have carried on to this day and are often recommended by those practicing natural medicines. Like juniper, manzanita is never used during pregnancy.

SPIRITUAL ASPECTS

Manzanita brings us an important lesson, and we learn it by watching how this variable shrub survives winter. This is a time of great flashing storms that blow out of the Arctic and often subject the plants and animals to great stresses which test their survival ability.

There are two ways that manzanita face this struggle. One is what I call The Way of the Oak and refers to many plants (and people) that brave the winter of life by standing up straight on a rigid scaffolding that will withstand the crushing weight of snow and ice. The other, I call The Way of the Willow: it involves the ability to flex and bend with the wind and elemental forces, then to spring back into form when the weight has eased off.

Some species of manzanita, such as *A. patula*, the green manzanita, are unbending and fixed in their ways, surviving through sheer force of will; whereas other species, such as our old friend kinnikinnik, can survive long periods submerged beneath a pillow of snow, which actually insulates them from extreme temperatures.

Just as my father was an Oak, he allowed me to be a Willow because he knew that both ways can see you through. It matters not if you choose The Way of the Oak or The Way of the Willow; both are Ways of the Warrior and have a needed place in our world.

If you should run across a piece of manzanita wood, hold it in your hand and spend some time rubbing its smooth surface. I was once given a small piece of manzanita which had been rounded smooth on both ends and fitted comfortably in the palm. Whenever I took it out of my medicine pouch and began feeling its God polished bark and wood, I could feel the tension and anger draining out of my body and mind and being transformed inside that crafted 'worry peg', as it was called. Just as, in the physical, manzanita works on the kidneys, so it has the ability to dispose of the emotional and mental metabolic waste of the spiritual body.

Carrying either the fruit, leaves or wood of this highly beneficial plant will help you clear out any impurities in your thinking or actions. It can serve as a reminder that we all choose our own way to survive this world and it is other people's problem if they do not respect that.

Smoking the leaves can bring you great insight and introspection even if you are not a Native American. If you are a human being, period, then you have the right. It is also possible to increase your psychic powers by making a weak tea from the leaves and soaking a handkerchief in it, then either applying the wrung-out material to the forehead or making a headband out of it to wear around your head when you wish to be more spiritually in tune.

Spiraea
(*Spiraea*, many species)

This is where I get to take a little bit of artistic license on the topic of medicinal bushes. This segment, although starting with spiraea, a common shrub found in many temperate gardens around Australia, will be stretched to include two perennials that were originally included in the genus but have now been given their own genus, *Filipendula*.

I do this for two reasons. The first is to demonstrate how the Native American use of medicinal herbs changed with the introduction of many herbs brought over from Europe during the colonization of the Americas, and how often these superseded original, time honored treatments, as was the case with spiraea.

The second reason is that I simply find the two species in the genus of *Filipendula* – meadowsweet and dropwort – so interesting and useful and just didn't have the space to include them in the section on the perennial Grandfathers. It seemed logical and appropriate to knit them together into one herbal cardigan.

Before the introduction of meadowsweet and dropwort, the two most commonly utilized species of *Spiraea* were hardhack (*S. tomentosa*) and *S. alba*, which, just to confuse the matter even more, was also known as meadowsweet.

PHYSICAL ASPECTS

A large group of flowering herbaceous perennials and shrubs with often feathery foliage and sprays of pink to white flowers usually in spring or summer. Spiraea shrubs vary from deciduous to nearly evergreen, produce attractive colored leaves and grow to about two meters.

MEDICINAL ASPECTS

The whole plant of both species – roots, stems, leaves and flowers – was considered an excellent tonic medicine, usually served up as a tea by Native Americans living along the north-eastern section of America.

The Mohegans, occupying what is now part of Connecticut, considered it a powerful astringent, useful in treating hemorrhages of the bowel, diarrhea, dysentery and cholera. The Ojibwas tended to use it more as a women's herb, and found it beneficial during childbirth to help speed the process and to reduce fever and inflammations. Further to the west the Osage, who called the shrub

Honskokaogacha, often chewed the dried roots and stems to staunch haemoptysis, a condition that causes one to spit blood. A cold infusion was taken by women as a douche for 'women's' complaints.

The meadowsweet shrub was a favorite tea of many early Indian nations, not only for its flavor (which was compared favorably with most other teas), but for its ability to reduce vomiting and nausea. Both of these shrubs were incorporated into the pharmacopoeia of the white settlers who also tried it on cases of ulcers and gonorrhea.

When these early immigrants began arriving on the shores of Turtle Island, they brought with them two popular medicinal perennials, the well-known meadowsweet (*Filipendula ulmaria*) and the not-so-well-known dropwort (*F. hexapetala*). These were used for much the same purposes that their bushy cousins, the spiraeas, were used for.

Both, however, contain much higher percentages of salicylic acid, the active ingredient in aspirin, which made them more effective as pain relievers and in the treatment of rheumatism, influenza and headaches. It wasn't long before these plants spread throughout the new land and quickly found a place in Native American herbal lore.

We find this often to be the case when new herbs are introduced from overseas that are in many respects better medicine than previously known indigenous plants. Nowadays, most Amerindians prefer taking *aspirin*, and the gracious shrub spiraea has been relegated to the nursery and landscaping trade.

There is some confusion as to whether salicylic acid was isolated from the willow or from meadowsweet. It was most probably found as a result of studying the pain-relieving constituents of both plants, although the name *aspirin* literally means 'from spiraea' so we can assume only that meadowsweet (originally called spiraea) got all the credit. You may also be interested to learn that the name *Spirea* comes from the Greek word *speiraira*, which means a plant used for garlands.

SPIRITUAL ASPECTS

Not all that long ago we had, as a society, a clear picture of what a man was and what a woman was, and how to interact within the roles we were given. We had very strong cultural rules within which most men conformed to the perception of what a man was, and the same for women. If you stepped over the boundary that separated the two sexes, you were, at worst, institutionalized or jailed, or, at best, ostracized. Both sexes are now in an era of total disorientation about our sexual beings. Nothing makes any sense any more, and we are cast into the abyss of confusion.

The spirit of the spiraea can bring us a new concept with which to establish our lives in the Fifth World, one based on love for all others and particularly ourselves. It is a world not so rigidly defining the sexes, for we move closer to achieving a total balance of male and female energies within each individual.

In the world of Spirit there is no sexual differentiation. It is only when we enter the physical world that we 'split' our spiritual identities, leaving only a lifelong desire to fill in the space. When we achieve perfect balance in the physical, we are free from the search.

Spiraea is the energy of perfect balance and harmony and all parts of the plant can be used to help attain equilibrium within your sexual being. Before you do any cutting or pulling of either spiraea or filipendula, it is important to spend some time in his company. Spring and summer is the best time to do this, particularly if they are in bloom. Sit down next to the plant as he tells you in mental pictures how you may best balance your sexual being. Look (really see) how the foliage and flowers achieve the perfect balance of texture and form. There are some particularly nice cultivars available now that have multi-colored foliage, providing striking contrasts.

The flowers are the most powerful part of the plant and can be cut and dried before putting them either on your prayer altar or in your medicine bag, which I imagine must be getting pretty full by now. Flowers of the meadowsweet, fresh or dried, can be placed on the altar to herald in a new love. They play a predominant part in many old love charms and potions. The white flowers of the bridal wreath spiraea, *S. prunifolia*, have been worn at weddings for centuries to show the commitment and purity of the bride.

Yucca
(*Yucca*, many species)

Most of the species of *yucca* growing throughout the United States and Mexico were considered the most generous of all the Grandfathers, for he provided much of the materials and medicines necessary for survival. This was particularly true for the native population of the south-west, the home of the Zuni, Hopi, Pueblo, Navajo, Apache, Pima and many other people.

The needles at the end of each leaf could be broken off, together with the fibre that peeled away, providing a needle and thread, all in one. When crushed, the leaves yielded a fibre that could be made into clothing, baskets, rope, twine, fishing nets, mattresses, bags and blankets. The flower buds were eaten raw or roasted over hot coals and served warm. The seeds were also roasted and ground into 'Indian bread' or mixed with sheep's milk and eaten like porridge. The young cluster of leaves at the center of a plant would be collected and cooked like cabbage.

PHYSICAL ASPECTS

Yucca is a very hardy and drought resistant shrub consisting of short-stemmed or stemless clumps covered with tough sword-like leaves. It produces long flower spikes bearing cream-colored blooms. Many plants reproduce through rosettes that form at the base of the parent plant.

MEDICINAL ASPECTS

The roots were pounded until sudsy, then used like a soap and shampoo. It not only cleaned the clothes, body and hair but was also reputed to stop hair loss. (Come to think of it, one doesn't see too many bald Native Americans.) It is best not to do this where the water is likely to run off into fish-populated waters as it often stuns and kills them.

Grated root was applied to areas of the body that were painfully inflamed with sprains or arthritis, a practice that seems to bear up under scientific scrutiny. It was also taken internally as a tea for the same affliction or in cases of stomach cramping.

SPIRITUAL ASPECTS

When I was a young man in search of my 'higher calling', I made a trek to the high desert country of Arizona. It is a land of vast beauty and wide open spaces where human beings can lose themselves or find themselves in its gentle harshness.

The wonderful Navajo (Dine) people occupy this part of the world and have always provided me with a wealth of humour and wisdom. For a Coyote like myself it has always felt like home.

On this, my third trip to Arizona, I camped near a sacred spot called Canyon De Chelly. This was where, years before, I had had one of my first truly 'mystical' experiences, and it has often beckoned me back.

On this trip I met a man who offered to show me around for a small fee. While exploring the bottom of the canyon we came to a place where there was a perfect circle of yucca plants. The location was obviously a place held sacred by these people, for you could see that much of it had been cleared and had an almost 'swept' appearance.

With as much humility as I could muster, I asked my guide whether this place had a special significance, to which he replied that it was a place where human beings could come to learn a great secret. He then asked me if I wanted to learn this mysterious secret, one which was held within this circle of plants. He already knew what my answer was going to be, for he stepped theatrically into the center of the circle and with the air of a great shaman pointed to the shrub growing in the east and said only 'yucca'. Going around the circle in a sun-wise direction he pointed to each of the plants and exclaimed the name over and over until I got the point. I now knew the great secret.

The Indians always had a place to live, a place to die, a place to cry and a place to laugh such as this place, for this was a magical circle of Indian laughing plants: yucca, yucca, yucca, yucca, yucca, yucca, yucca, yucca.

The greatest enemy of negativity is laughter. It is like a bright, shining light that drives away the darkness of evil things and deeds. This is a profound lesson that the spirit of the yucca gives, and he gives them freely to anyone who is not afraid to laugh. Laughter is the best medicine.

The soap that can be extracted from the yucca root is one of the most powerful tools in 'washing out' negativity and disease. It can be used in a ceremonial way to cleanse the body and energy field of mental, emotional and spiritual 'dirt' and help prevent illness or negativity from returning.

Some Native Americans still have the ability to 'shape shift' – that is, turn themselves into an animal or some other creature – at will. This is done after many years' apprenticeship and with a great deal of physical, mental, emotional and spiritual training. One of the tools in this practice is a hoop or wreath made from yucca fibers, which is either worn on the head or jumped through to facilitate the transformation.

Seven sacred flowers

Agrimony
(Agrimonia gryposepala, A. eupatoria)

While most people think of agrimony as a European herb, there are many species of this plant growing throughout the northern hemisphere.

I find it one of the more pleasant tasting teas and add it to many others to improve taste.

PHYSICAL ASPECTS

A delicate looking but tough herbaceous perennial with sharply pinnate aromatic leaves and small but bright yellow flowers borne on elongated racemes in summer. They grow to approximately sixty centimeters, with an almost equal spread when mature.

Although the seeds are not always easy to germinate, agrimony grows well in most sunny or partly shaded areas and makes a lovely addition to any garden.

MEDICINAL ASPECTS

Although agrimony was used in many different ways in the Native American culture, it had a well-established reputation as being a general tonic, particularly in cases of liver, kidney and gall bladder disorders.

The Ojibwe from the Great Lakes region of Canada found the root a useful ingredient in the treatment of certain urinary conditions. The Meskwake, Potawatomi and Winnabagos gathered fresh leaves of the plant to stop nosebleed, simply inserting them in the affected nostril for relief. Most of the tribes living in proximity to one of the many species of agrimony took advantage of its astringent qualities in the treatment of slow-healing wounds, burns and inflammation of the throat, and internally for diarrhea and bowel complaints, in lowering fevers and to help retain urine for those who were incontinent. I have even heard of it mixed with the paunch fat of swine as a sort of 'backwater Band-Aid', although I have no personal experience with this interesting concoction.

I have, however, had good success relieving sore throats with a gargle of the leaves, particularly when mixed with an equal amount of red raspberry leaves, as well as including it in my annual spring tonic brew, which consists of equal parts of dandelion and dock root, stinging nettle, red raspberry leaves, sarsaparilla if I can find it, and of course agrimony. For me it really helps to clear out even the worst case of winter sludge. This recipe has a very interesting story behind it that I would like to relate.

In the region of Pennsylvania where my great-grandfather, Nathan Bear White, was born, there was a large settlement of German immigrants who were led by a man named Joseph Doddridge. Rather than trying to displace the local Indian population, these people went to the native people asking to be taught their herbs, ceremonies and sacred practices. They then combined this with their own ancient Germanic knowledge and created a community that practiced many of the medicine ways that at one time bound all original cultures to the way of the Earth.

What makes this even more fascinating to me is that many of the sacred rituals, incantations, spells and healing formulas of both cultures were nearly identical and little adapting was necessary. Even the concept of the pow-wow was known to the community as an ancient Germanic ceremony long before they participated in it with the Native Americans. The synchronicity of cultures was also evident within the similarities in their spring tonics, both of course containing agrimony.

SPIRITUAL ASPECTS

Agrimony is a very powerful and protective ally, one that can banish even the nastiest curse or hex and send it back from whence it came. It has been known to Europeans and Native Americans as a herb that will render any negativity null and void if carried around in a medicine bag or pouch.

When in bloom, agrimony is like a candle in a dark room, illuminating all that its light can touch. While there are many in the physical and spiritual world that would like to see his light go out, it cannot be extinguished. He will always guide you to right thoughts and actions, and will transmit your honesty and good intentions to all those you come in contact with. For this reason, fibers from this plant are often combined with other materials such as willow and cane to make baskets, not only for the unusual yellow–gold coloring, but also to attract customers.

If you enjoy selling craft items, or anything else for that matter, it might be wise to find some agrimony to wear on your person while out selling, or sprinkle on the items you wish to sell water in which you have boiled agrimony flowers. If you sell used cars, remember that this herb promotes honest intention in all you do. You might want to leave it at home. If you have trouble getting to sleep, you might try putting a small bag of agrimony under your pillow. It is said to help promote a peaceful and protected sleep.

Angelica

(Angelica, many species*).*

We find different species of angelica in many parts of the world, and the claims made for this large, mostly biennial genus of herbs in healing a wide range of ailments is almost second to none.

PHYSICAL ASPECTS

The genus of *Angelica* consists of mainly large herbaceous biennials which produce bold, widely-divided dark green leaves from a central shoot the first year, and enormous stalked flower umbels the second. The multitude of small whitish flowers spawns abundant seeds which fall as the plant begins to die.

MEDICINAL ASPECTS

The dried root and seeds have long been prescribed by healers for digestive problems and in stabilizing menstrual irregularities. The Chinese angelica, *Angelica sinensis* or *dong quai*, is said to be particularly effective in balancing female hormones. All species are warming in effect and therefore considered helpful in many bronchial problems.

The Native American population had several different species of this shade- and water-loving genus. The most prevalent and popular species was (and still is) *A. atropurpurea*, commonly referred to as purple-stem angelica, Osha del Campo, and bellyache root. The last name alludes to its use by the Creeks who made a tea from the root to treat indigestion, flatulent colic and (of course) bellyaches. The Cherokee preferred to administer it for colds and fevers, to strengthen nervous, worn-out females, and as a warming agent to help increase the flow of blood to the extremities in cases of extreme exposure and frostbite. The Menomini made a hot compress for specific bodily pains by mashing the cooked roots and adding in a dash of sagebrush (*Artemisia canadensis*), then applied it opposite the affected area in order to let the pain 'escape'.

To many of the Indian nations living along the western coastal regions of North America, angelica was employed for so many ailments that in some cases it was just about the only herb used to treat illnesses. The dried roots hung in every door, not only for household medicinal use, but also to ward off any malevolent ghosts and to appease the spirits. Planting the seed yearly is important if you desire a regular supply of angelica root. As I said earlier, most biennials live for only two years before setting seed and dying. Angelica seed is very short-lived and should be planted as soon as possible. If kept tightly sealed in the refrigerator the seed can last for up to a year before viability really begins to suffer. **A word of caution here about using the root of the angelica fresh: without being cooked or dried it can be highly poisonous,** and in fact many Native American people resorted to ingesting the fresh root in order to commit ritual suicide. This can be a very painful way to go and is definitely not an advisable thing to do. Maybe all you need is a change of luck.

SPIRITUAL ASPECTS

Did you say you need a change of luck for the better? Then have I got a charm for you, for the angelica root is one of the best good luck talismans I know of.

The dried root of this plant has been carried as a charm for as long as there has been gambling amongst Native Americans, which is probably a good long time. With more and more casinos opening up on reservations throughout the United States, it's not unusual to see players fondling their Osha del Campo root as they play a game of blackjack or yank on the levers of the 'one-armed bandits' (slot machines).

It is said that the famous gambler/gamboler Kokopelli won the city of Pueblo Bonito due to the strength of his root, both literally and figuratively, but that's another story.

On a more serious note, the angelica root is considered highly sacred to native people and shavings are often mixed with tobacco in pipe ceremonies, or cast onto the hot coals of the sweat lodge during purification. It was a common practice of healers to chew on a small bit of root when visiting contagiously sick patients, in the belief that it warded off disease. Europeans also believed in this practice, acquiring its botanical name of *A. archangelica* when the Archangel Raphael appeared before a French monk and told him that, by using this herb, he could fend off the plague which was at that time ravaging the population of Europe.

For the hunters who often spent weeks or months in the forest in search of deer and other prey to bring back to the village, the angelica root was indispensable. Its scent was used primarily to mask their own scent and to attract the game animals, and hunters were constantly rubbing it between their palms and applying it to their entire bodies. This is still common practice on many reservations where the traditional ways have been revived.

Although I have never been a hunter, angelica has often served me well when fishing. Whether it just masks my human smell from the bait or actually attracts the fish with the scent, I cannot say, but it certainly seems to have some positive effect on my efforts.

I find that the smell of a dried angelica root is very intoxicating, almost addictive. Once I start sniffing it, I don't want to stop. This might be useful to those addicted to cigarettes, as an aid to giving them up. When you feel like a smoke, try getting out your angelica root, have a few deep draughts of its fragrance and call in a helpful spirit to assist you through the craving.

Angelica roots are among the important links between us and the Spirit world. In our present culture we are only just beginning to understand and rekindle the connection that needs to exist between those who have been freed from the material plane and those of us that remain here to learn our important spiritual lessons.

Most, if not all, native cultures of the world practice the philosophy of praying to their departed relations or other spirits of the etheric realm for help in a difficult situation or in giving thanks for the abundance around us. This in no way goes against the teachings of the worshipping of one God, for it has always been acknowledged that there is only one true God, and this Great Mysterious has many helpers that are our closest connection to God and each other.

We need not be afraid of these spiritual beings if we are of good heart, for they are here to guide us, protect us and offer us unconditional love.

Cohosh, blue and black
(*Cimifuga racemosa* and *Caulophyllum thalictrioides*)

Although the black cohosh and blue cohosh are in no way related, I decided to group them together for the sake of saving space and sneaking in an extra herb. They are both employed for similar purposes, but are different enough for each to warrant its own credit.

PHYSICAL ASPECTS

Blue cohosh is an unusual and rare herbaceous perennial often growing as a single purple leaf-stalk which unfolds as it opens, closely followed by a cluster of star-shaped flowers which in turn produce dark blue berries. The plant rarely grows taller than seventy-five centimeters.

Black cohosh, in contrast, will often grow to over two meters and produces long wand-like racemes of white star-burst flowers. The shiny dark green divided leaves appear from a central clump which spreads slowly with age. It, too, is a herbaceous perennial.

Both grow in a woodland environment and are happy if given seventy-five per cent shade.

MEDICINAL ASPECTS

Black cohosh, or black snakeroot as it is often called, was often referred to as a female's herb as it was commonly given to women to facilitate childbirth, increase the flow of breast milk and promote menstruation. However, it provided men with the ability to reduce or relieve rheumatism and arthritis. The root decoction was found useful in treating many illnesses such as gonorrhea or vaginal irritations. Early settlers to eastern America quickly learned from the Native population of its marvellous ability to subdue life-threatening lung conditions such as croup, pneumonia and asthma, and thought it one of the best bush medicines that had yet been found in the New World.

The medical profession of the 1800s adopted the use of black cohosh for an incredible array of disorders, including hysteria, whooping cough, measles, scarlet fever and seminal emissions.

Blue cohosh was frequently used either by itself or in conjunction with black cohosh. Both shared the common name of squaw root, but now it is considered very rude to use the word *squaw*, since its true translation has been revealed to be of a sensitive female sexual nature.

The most frequent use of this striking blue-leaved and flowered perennial was in preparation for a quick and pain-free (well, almost) delivery for women approaching the last few weeks of pregnancy. Like black cohosh it was also employed for rheumatism and arthritis, but a tea of the root was administered in cases of cramps, epilepsy, sore throats and some types of urinary problems, and particularly in reducing fevers. One treatment for gall-stones involved putting a smashed root into a cup of hot water and drinking it until vomiting took place.

SPIRITUAL ASPECTS

When we have problems accepting love into our lives, whether it be due to feelings of inadequacy or a fear we have of showing our true selves to another human being, we can turn the emotional symptoms into all sorts of illnesses or dis-eases.

We repress many functions that are natural to the body, such as breathing, fighting infection and (for women) childbirth and the moon cycle of the womb. When these functions are repressed we often fight ourselves to keep them repressed and many types of illness begin to manifest themselves due to the conflict being waged inside.

It is only when we consider ourselves to be worthy of self love and of love and respect from others for who and what we are that we release these repressed functions. If you are alive, then God must think you worthy to live a life free from pain and suffering. All of us, no matter how sick or despondent, can benefit from accepting ourselves for what we truly are – lumps, bumps and all.

Cohosh works physically by releasing the energy that you have withheld so that the flow of natural bodily functions is restored to normal. In much the same way it frees up any etheric blockages about worthiness or ability, and helps foster an acceptance and loving of our shortcomings and attributes. To love and accept yourself means loving all of you: the good and the not so good.

The spirits of the cohosh wish to instill in each one of us a seed of encouragement. Once planted, it may take some time and patience before his gift germinates, for it often takes several cold winters before it begins to emerge. When it becomes established in our heart's garden, it will slowly send out rhizomes of love and affection away from itself in an ever-increasing range. It is never aggressive, only slow and sure, but spread and multiply it does. Soon you will have love and acceptance enough to begin to spread the gift around. Do not be impatient, for all good and growing things take time to mature.

When you feel you are ready for a whole relationship, draw yourself a nice hot bath and add to it a few sprinkles of cohosh, blue or black. If it is in tincture form, place seven drops in the bath before settling in, and make sure you are not disturbed. After you have soaked long enough to become totally relaxed, or as relaxed as you get, bring the water up to your face in cupped hands and visualize the person you would like to share love with. As you slowly pour the water on your face, try to get a good mental picture of you and the other person talking or simply enjoying each other's company. Do this four times, one for each of the four directions, and at the end include a prayer of thanks. If you are indeed ready to commit to true love, you will find it soon after.

Echinacea
(*Echinacea angustifolia, E. pallida, E. purpurea*)

There are now available at health food stores, and more recently seen at chemists and even supermarkets, dozens of herbal preparations that had their origins in Native American medical knowledge and practice. The list now includes such familiar plants as evening primrose, bergamot, black and blue cohosh, creosote bush, blue flag, milkweed, goldenseal and many more. None, however, has enjoyed the level of success and acceptability that echinacea has.

Ten years ago, when I would mention this fine medicinal plant, most people would get a glazed look in their eyes that denoted they had no idea what I was talking about, and most likely they would forget the name once out of sight. Now this herb is on the tip of everyone's tongue, literally and figuratively, and even allopathic medicine has begun to embrace it as part of a more holistic approach to health.

This herb has done more for herbal medicine than any other, for it has started the construction of a bridge of understanding between conventional medicines and natural healing methods. Now it is not unusual for a GP to recommend the use of this herb rather than resorting to antibiotics, which are rapidly losing their effectiveness against many types of infections. It brings us closer to establishing a system of health care that brings in the best of both worlds, as well as a tool to increase our ability to be more self-empowered in the choices we are given concerning what we put into our bodies.

There are nine or ten (depending on who you speak to) species of *Echinacea*, but the most popular and available species are the narrowleaf echinacea, *E. angustifolia*; the pale-purple coneflower,

E. pallida; and the purple cone-flower, *E. purpurea*. If you look carefully at the labels of echinacea products you will see that by far the most commonly used species is the purple coneflower. This, unfortunately, has nothing to do with which species is the best, but rather reflects the ease with which it can be economi-cally propagated, grown and harvested compared with the other two species. Whole fields of the purple coneflower can be planted by simply broadcasting the seed and watering, and harvesting is often done by cutting the crop of its leaves and flowers and waiting for the plants to re-sprout from the root and crown of the plant which are left intact. Several harvests a year are possible using this method and the return is quite good.

The two other species, *E. pallida* and *E. angustifolia*, produce a seed that is far more costly and difficult to propagate, requiring several months of stratifying at about five degrees Celsius before they will germinate. This is usually hand-planted, making for a very labor-inten-sive process. It is always the root that is harvested on these two species, requiring the whole plants to be dug up after two years of growing and usually (but not always) replanting after each harvest. It is the eco-nomics of growing echinacea that has determined the cheapest and most readily available source. In my opinion, the purple coneflower is the least effective of the lot, although still a marvellous herb.

Every Native American nation within the growing habitat of echinacea held it in high esteem and it was utilized probably more than any other herb on the prairie. Within Native American circles the roots of *E. angustifolia* and *E. pallida* were considered a valu-able commodity for trading with friendly nations to the south, such as the Mayans and Toltecs of Mexico.

PHYSICAL ASPECTS

A small genus of herbaceous perennials known for their showy violet to purple daisy-like flowers which are produced in summer. The slightly fuzzy leaves are lance-shaped in some species, such as *E. angustifolia*, and more ovate in others, like *E. purpurea*.

MEDICINAL ASPECTS

It has been most commonly used for strengthening the immune system during the onset of symptoms of colds, coughs, 'flu or any other communicable illness, and was considered an antidote for the bite or sting of any venomous creature. It was also chewed to alleviate fatigue and pain during long hunting or raiding parties and is still used today during the long, gruelling Sun Dance.

The most frequent method of administration was the simplest: taking a piece of fresh root and chewing it, allowing the medicinal juice slowly to work its way down the throat. In this manner the anti-viral, anti-bacterial qualities of the plant would go to where they were most needed. For toothache, a piece of the root was placed next to the affected tooth and left there until the pain subsided.

Another method of taking in the curative qualities was by burning the dry root and inhaling the smoke. This was generally done in cases of upper respiratory tract infections and headache. It was also frequently made into a tea and given to treat swollen glands, burns, hydrophobia, tonsillitis and pain in the lower digestive tract as well as for rheumatism, arthritis and general inflammation of the joints.

If ever there was a panacea for nearly every complaint, echinacea has to be it. Sadly, though, much of the natural stands of this herb have been greatly reduced due to the demand for its root. Harvesters of wild herbs have legally dug up about as much as they can, and now we are faced with a great shortage of *E. angustifolia* and *E. pallida* as well as creating an ecological hole throughout the prairie lands of the United States.

My hope is that we will all become guardians of our own health and grow as much of this fine and colorful herb as is needed to heal ourselves and the great open prairie.

SPIRITUAL ASPECTS

It is no accident that, after at least four hundred years of knowing about echinacea, our culture is only now beginning to recognize the incredible gift that this rugged herb brings to us. It has come just in the nick of time, for not only are we now exposed to new and virulent strains of pathogens but also we have seen an end to the use of many, once powerful anti-biotics.

Penicillin saved my life as a two-year-old with an infection spreading close to the frontal lobe, but if this affliction were to strike me today, the same medication would be far less likely to do the job. Many, if not most, infectious agents are now quite tolerant of the array of available antibiotics, and the future looks ever bleaker. We have played the last few hands in the great antibiotic card game, and it happens just when echinacea becomes the password.

Unlike antibiotics, echinacea helps us fight our own war on bacteria and viruses by boosting the natural defenses that were part of the great scheme of things from the beginning. The whole body seems to sense even the presence of this age-old remedy and often rallies its energies for the job ahead.

Our mental, emotional and spiritual bodies have become infected, too, by what, in the 1960s, was called 'Future Shock'. We human beings can only take so much of anything, yet we now live in an age of global communication that supplies an overload of news, learning and scientific advancement. The world keeps speeding up and we have few ways to deal with it. Our etheric bodies are filled to capacity with informational pathogens, and the sicknesses our society is feeling are a reflection of this internal invasion.

Our etheric bodies, like our physical ones, have the ability to cope with this type of spiritual infection. Our incorporeal 'immune system', called prayer or meditation, which are the same thing, can be turned on in times of great stress. Real prayer, like meditation, quietens our mind so that we can better hear the word of God. Certainly we always give thanks and ask for things in prayer, but that's only half of it. The other half is quietly waiting for the answer, even if it is 'no'.

Echinacea is one of the best tools I have ever used in this regard. I easily grow about a hundred plants a year in a rather small space, and know that they are always at work cleansing my thoughts and the environmental clutter that we are all barraged with. Sitting amongst the purple splendor of these plants, I feel their color enter and virtually dance around my crown chakra, picking up random pieces of mental, emotional and spiritual pathogens that have entered my etheric system, absorbing their poisons and transforming negativity into immunity.

It doesn't matter if you have one plant or thousands – the effect is still the same. The spirit of echinacea guards over us and comes to our aid when we are etherically infected. It raises our vibration to better filter out the extemporaneous clutter.

Holding a small piece of echinacea root while in prayer or meditation will help you to center more on the here and now, and allow you to move more peacefully into the quiet. It will help eliminate negative thoughts and emotions that are a bane to close communication with the Creator and our Spirit helpers.

If you can grow a little extra echinacea each year, think about drying a few of the roots and sending some of it up to the heavens in the form of smoke to give thanks for all the Creator has given us.

Ginseng
(Panax quinquefolia)

One might think that, for the many people who were the original caretakers of ginseng's natural habitat, all the recent publicity and fanfare about the excellent qualities of American ginseng, about how useful it appears to be in treating a wide range of ailments and afflictions, would have represented quite a medical cornucopia. In actual fact, ginseng, although certainly a popular general tonic and external poultice for open sores and wounds, was never considered as valuable as its European counterparts.

Native American nations such as those in the Iroquois Confederacy were paid great sums of money or 'wampum' for this herb, particularly by the French, who would then in turn sell it at great profit to the Chinese. For most of the Amerindians living in the eastern third of North America, collecting ginseng for the Europeans became a popular pastime in the mid-1700s, and it wasn't long before things got right out of control.

As supplies became scarce, tribes began encroaching on their neighbors' territory, looking for this botanical gold mine. Conflict inevitably followed, and was of course always encouraged by the French and British colony builders.

Within a century, much of the delicate stands of ginseng were gone, traded off for cash or prized European inventions like metal tools and weapons or glass beads. A few Indian nations, like the Ojibwas, did make an effort to replant the seeds after pulling up the root, but wild American ginseng became as rare as the Tasmanian tiger and was encountered about as frequently.

Most of the commercial ginseng from the United States is grown in Wisconsin. Ironically, two early Australian growers of American ginseng, Fred and Charlene Hosemans, began their planting near my home in Victoria. It is a true test of devotion to one's dreams to grow a herb that takes five to seven years before it yields any harvest.

PHYSICAL ASPECTS

A small but hardy herbaceous perennial with divided leaves of three to seven lobed leaflets growing from a single central shoot. The small white flowers in spring are followed by raspberry-shaped fruit. Ginseng rarely exceeds sixty centimeters in height.

MEDICINAL ASPECTS

It is known that most native people did use this herb in one way or another, but certainly not to the extent of their Chinese cousins. The Cherokee used it for coughs (as an expectorant), headaches, cramps, convulsions, tuberculosis and festering sores whilst the Houmas mixed it with whisky and drank the cocktail to ease rheumatic pain. A great-

uncle of mine used to swear by this treatment, without the ginseng, and said as long as he was drinking it, he felt no pain. Many tribes found the ginseng cocktail useful in calming an upset stomach and to stimulate the appetite.

There are two reasons why ginseng was not used more extensively by the Native American population. First, it must be understood that the average Indian was, particularly by European standards, of robust health and well-being. There was little stress, pollution or disease in pre-Columbian times, the food was abundant and nourishing, and their system of public health benefits and techniques of preventative medicine created societies that were happy and healthy. We find far greater benefit today in its use as a superb tonic, said to increase vitality and mental function as well as improving resistance to illness and disease. It is another herb whose time has come. Physical contaminants, such environmental pollution, and stress, have taken a great toll on our society, and as these increase, so will the need for herbs like ginseng. We also need to look at what other 'tonics' would improve our society.

Second, ginseng was far more utilized as a spiritual medicine and often found itself involved in cures, curses, love potions and spell casting. It was always considered big medicine, but more commonly in the spiritual sense.

SPIRITUAL ASPECTS

One of the 'little' uses of this 'big' medicine was as a fishing lure of sorts. Fishing hooks and line were soaked overnight in a bowl containing water and sliced-up ginseng root. Fishermen would hold a piece of the root in the mouth and chew on it throughout the day, using the spit to mask the human smell from the hands and bait.

A bigger medicine was made by drinking a potion of ginseng to create illness in other people. This is a darker side to the magic and witchcraft that was employed by many Amerindians to gain power or prestige, or to thwart an enemy. For every spell there would usually be a counter-spell made from the same herb, and its application often made the difference between life and death for those stricken by 'black magic'.

A decoction was also rubbed on the extremities of Iroquois ball players to thwart a rival team and the dried root was part of the medicine bundle of many spiritual healers. It was known as a sexual lure and was carried to ensure virility and to draw in and radiate the energy of love. It was said to make the owner more attractive.

A practice of the great Cherokee healers of not so long ago was to use ginseng to 'protect' any part of the body from being re-infected by a bad spirit or illness upon completion of a cure. For instance, if you had an evil spirit affecting your spleen, the healer would first 'exorcise' the spirit from the afflicted spleen and then, after chewing up a piece of ginseng root to a fine mash, would spray the content of his or her mouth onto your corresponding body area to 'seal' the spleen from further attack. Once you got used to the idea of somebody spitting on you, it could be a very effective method.

Ginseng not only helps to cleanse the etheric body and clean out deep buried pollutants, it also sets up a vibrational barrier that helps to reduce the amount of negative energy we absorb in our daily lives. He protects and shelters us from the ravages of modern society, such as stress and hectic lifestyle, and opens us up to beneficial healing powers of our Earthmother. He does not offer any quick fixes; rather, he works slowly and methodically to facilitate his work and requires us to do the same if we are to heal ourselves.

Goldenseal
(Hydrastis canadensis)

When I said earlier that, had it not been for penicillin, I probably would have died at age two, I was speaking about what was currently available to conventional medicine at the time. Had it been two hundred years ago, or two thousand years ago in my ancestral Cherokee home, I would have most likely been treated internally and topically with goldenseal.

With the help and skill of the medicine man, I would have undoubtedly been up and about in no time, and there is a good chance that while playing I would have been protected from insect bites with a combination of goldenseal and bear grease.

PHYSICAL ASPECTS

A low-growing herbaceous perennial which produces small whitish flowers and rounded red 'fruit' from the center of its palmate leaves. It grows to a height of about forty centimeters.

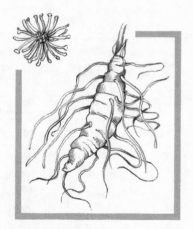

Two years of alternating warm and cold cycles are often needed before the seed germinates, and the seedlings are challenging to grow. Once established it is actually quite easy to divide the rootlets that form around the parent plant, although you need a supply of plants to start with and a bit of patience. My efforts at growing goldenseal in Gembrook have, to date, been fairly limited, only due to time and money.

MEDICINAL ASPECTS

Traditionally, this was a highly respected herb, one that lived in the dark, cool hardwood forest floor and provided Native Americans with a valuable antiseptic good for internal and external infections. It was also a precious tonic that was said to cure even cancer. It was claimed by many peoples, from the Seminoles of southern Florida to the Algonquin of eastern Canada, to be effective in soothing infected and inflamed tissue, particularly beneficial in cases involving mucous membranes. Often used as an eyewash, the mashed root was also applied to wounds to staunch the flow of blood and reduce the chance of infection. The root was also chewed to heal mouth ulcers whilst a tea was employed as a douche to clear up vaginal infections.

Mixed with other herbs it has been said to cure everything from venereal disease to tuberculosis and its reputation became widespread throughout America and Europe. Once again, demand for the herb decimated the natural stand of this shade-loving perennial. It was never very prolific and by the late 1800s it became quite rare. There are still those who go out and illegally collect what little goldenseal there is left. The only hope is that many people will begin growing this inestimable treasure of the forest.

My feeling about goldenseal is similar to that about other herbs whose time has either come or is near. We are likely to see goldenseal become even more of a precious commodity as skin ailments resistant to many conventional drugs begin to increase.

It is said to be effective against both gram negative and gram positive bacteria which are infecting our hospitals at alarming rates. Giardiasis is now a well-known illness in Australia, particularly in Sydney where it recently became a serious health threat, and goldenseal has shown promise in treating this potentially fatal condition. As new strains of influenza continue, this herb could be a valuable tool in the fight, and, used with other herbs, could even save lives.

SPIRITUAL ASPECTS

The most significant traditional usage of goldenseal was centered not so much on the medicinal qualities of the herb as on the spiritual characteristics that the Creator endowed this plant with.

The spirit of goldenseal is a very strong protector, and this energy is expressed on the physical plane through the brilliant golden-yellow dye that comes from the roots. This dye was used to paint the bodies and armaments of the warriors in the belief that it created an etheric shield to protect them in battle. The dye was employed by some medicine men to help send a hex to another person – not to injure or kill them, but to teach them a lesson about life. These hexes often resulted in the 'victim' having to change their ways completely, due to the catastrophes that had befallen them, but it was always to bring love and light into their lives, not to destroy.

Goldenseal was also taken to cancel love medicines and spells when they went wrong, as they occasionally did. In one case I heard about, a young man decided to use love medicine to secure the affections of a beautiful Indian maiden and did so by rubbing a certain plant on what he believed to be her clothing while it was hanging out to dry. Unfortunately, it turned out that, on that day, her less than desirable sister was drying her clothes, so it was she who accidentally received the spell. The poor young man could be seen making every effort to stay away from this unwanted suitor, but to no avail. She was all over him like wet buckskin and there just weren't enough places to hide. It was only after he 'paid' the medicine man a few prime pelts that the spell was undone by bathing his entire head in a goldenseal potion and ceremonially drinking the liquid until throwing up, thereby losing the spell.

You can use goldenseal leaves, roots or tincture to set up your own etheric shield by mixing it with rain or pure spring water and ceremonially washing yourself, starting at the base chakra and working your way up, visualizing a golden white light of protection enveloping you from your feet to the top of your head. You do not have to use great quantities of this precious liquid – just putting a few drops in your palms and rubbing them together will be enough to apply the energy to your auric field. You do not actually have to wet your body in this way, although I tend towards the dramatic and like to apply it quite liberally on the physical as well as the spiritual body. This is obviously best done outside or in the bathtub or shower since the liquid tends to stain carpet and clothes.

Sage
(*Salvia,* many species)

How appropriate it is that we finish off this humble section on herbs with the genus of *Salvia*, the true sages of the plant kingdom. Over 900 species of salvia are represented worldwide and I have yet to find one that is not used in some way, physically or etherically, to heal the mind, body and spirit.

PHYSICAL ASPECTS

A large genus comprised of over 900 species worldwide, sage consists of annuals, biennials, perennials and mostly evergreen shrubs. The aromatic leaves vary from ovate to lanceolate and are often grey or light green in color. Flowers are produced in spike and can be red, blue, white, pink or purple, depending on species. Sage plants range in height from forty centimeters to over two meters.

MEDICINAL ASPECTS

If one were to generalize about the medicinal powers of this huge group of plants, it could be said that many species are made into tea and taken to relieve digestive problems and soothe mucous membranes. Generalizations in this case, however, can be quite misleading and dangerous, for there are a number of species of sage that, if taken internally, will put you somewhere you may not want to be. Many, like *S. divinora*, are highly hallucinogenic and have been used traditionally for thousands of years to induce visions. Other species are relatively benign and just make a good-tasting cup of tea or supply seasoning to stews, soups and meat products. You really want to have a clear intent when using this herb and know what species you are dealing with, or the effects you desire could be less than pleasant. Even the venerable Mediterranean sage, *S. officinalis*, can be hallucinogenic in large doses.

In order to cover the subject of this herb adequately, I would have to write a whole book on it, a task I would rather leave to experts. Native Americans, particularly those living in the western third of North America, still make use of the dozens of indigenous species. The most revered of the sages has always been the white or grandfather sage, *S. apiana*, which grows throughout the coastal foothills of California.

The leaves of this very fragrant shrub have been used as a shampoo and hair straightener, and I often crush a leaf in my palms and apply it to my underarms as a deodorant. It not only smells incredibly intoxicating but also seems to reduce perspiration. Just the fumes given off by this plant are enough to open up blocked sinuses and give relief to 'flu symptoms.

The seeds of grandfather sage were often gathered in the old days and roasted for eating. The seeds of the diminutive annual, chia (*S. hispanica*), were also collected, roasted and ground in large numbers by many California tribes, often soaked in water and drunk as a highly nutritive food supplement to be taken during long forced marches, and was a popular folk remedy for diarrhea. Another species common to California is fragrant sage, or *S. clevelandii*, whose leaves are still used as a seasoning for wild or domestic game, particularly fowl. Azure sage, *S. azurea* 'Grandiflora', growing in central North America, was frequently used by the Cheyenne, Sioux, Crow and Pawnee as well as many other nomadic dwellers of the Great Plains, not only to reduce sweating and decrease lactation in women who were weaning their children, but also as a stomach calming tonic and toner. The roots of another, much smaller perennial which flourished in the eastern third of North America, lyre-leaf sage, or *S. lyrata*, was considered a cancer cure by the Cherokee, who passed it on to the early settlers, who also had similar success. The red-veined leaves were made into a tea to treat diarrhea, coughs, colds and general weakness. They were also picked when fresh to rub on bites and stings.

Again let me stress that different sages have different effects and it is always wise to consult a higher authority before self administering any unknown species.

SPIRITUAL ASPECTS

The spirit of salvia is the adhesive that binds all of humanity. Wherever you travel in the world you will find its many and varied people practicing the ancient spiritual expression of thanksgiving through the act of smudging. It is a universal concept, one that permeates cultures both prehistoric and contemporary. The burning of a sage leaf to release the fragrant white cloud of smoke, sending billowing prayers towards the heavens, brings in spirits of love and light, and passing the smoke over the body to purify mind, body and spirit have all been aspects of our desire to bring a heavenly existence to the Earthly plane.

The white sage or grandfather sage has aided immeasurably in bringing harmony and spiritual 'presence' to my life. We both share the same name (White, not grandfather) and were born to the same geographical location. I had my first smudge at seven years of age from this grandfather of Grandfathers, and something in my life shifted. I awakened to the silent voices of my forefathers – not just

Native American but of many people and races and times, for I am of many people and ancestors. Dutch, Moorish, Irish, German and who knows what else have been homogenized in my blood, and it doesn't really matter.

For as long as we have all wandered the Earth seeking to reunite our cultures, we have been linked by the sacred traditions that have been handed down to every nation on the planet. Pray, for we are all one voice to God. Quest, for we all have a vision that needs to be uncovered. Fast and sweat, so that your temple is as unpolluted as your soul and to show your commitment to the sacred journey. Make smoke offerings as a way to purify the mind, body and spirit, for they are all one. Take part in community ceremonies which acknowledge and honor the cycle of the seasons, moon, planets and stars, for we are all one.

These are five responsibilities which we need to return to if we are to reunite as one in the Fifth World. They are common to us all, and the lack we feel in our lives comes not from the external world around us, but from deep inside, longing to return to that place where once again we all join hands around the Tree of Life.

PART 5

the future of
herbal healing

A vision into the fifth world

I had a dream several years ago, when I was in the process of putting together the first Herbs of the World nursery here in my home region of Gembrook. In my dream I was in a room with four other people, none of whom I recognized. I was in the room observing when another person, whom I knew was a 'client', entered through a doorway and sat down on a large pillow.

The first to speak was a medical practitioner seated immediately to the right of the 'client'. He spoke to the person about the physical manifestations of disease and what form it had taken in his body. He could prescribe herbs, drugs or surgery to help stabilize the man's condition, but only after consultation with the remaining occupants of the room.

The second person to speak was someone like a shaman who spoke slowly about the journey that he would take the man on, a voyage into the hidden regions of his emotional cortex to view the damage that had been done to him.

The third was a woman with the ability to probe into the person's psyche and bring him to the light of self-analysis and introspection, helping him learn to solve his own problems.

The fourth appeared to be a holy man or 'praying man' as I have heard them respectfully referred to at pow-wow. He would pray for the man and teach him how to re-align his energy and balance. He might teach him a new healing song or, if it was meant to be, would teach him a death song to help him move out of this life.

Most of the people entering this room would leave already in the process of healing and few would need to come back once health had been restored. It cost nothing for it was known that if one person is ill, all are less well, and one of the best investments for a healthy society is to ensure a healthy citizenry.

In the world outside this room, herbs, fruit and vegetables grew in abundance everywhere, and no household was without a well-stocked pantry and medicine chest. Herbal medicine and what we now call conventional medicine were all facets in the gemstones of health care. Other facets included 'hands on healing' or Reiki-like application of healing energy radiating from the palms of the hands, drumming and chanting, acupressure and acupuncture as well as some lesser-known techniques of healing yet to emerge from the darkness of the nine periods of Hell.

There was no further action in the dream. Although it was very short, it was one of those dreams that had a certain quality to it that I recognize as an 'effective dream', one that has the possibility to unfold through the Will. That is, bringing it into the physical world through doing would make it a reality. Sometimes, as with the visions of Black Elk, dreams take some time to become manifest, but it is important never to let go of the dream or vision.

If we can extrapolate the future from the many prophecies that have been handed down through the ages by many cultures, we can see only two roads. We can continue down the 'easy' path towards self-destruction and find ourselves in a world dominated by insects; or we change, and come back to the understanding that we are all related to each other and the world around us and every other thing in existence.

When we begin to treat others as equals regardless of anything, and give the same respect to the Earth and her inhabitants, we will all come together as we once were, and share with each other that which we have learned over the ages since we became separated. In sharing and learning we will give our children and their children, and human beings through the next thirteen periods of Heaven, a legacy of peace, abundance and spiritual freedom.

Bibliography

Balls, Edward K. *Early Uses of California Plants*. University of California Press, 1962.

Bown, Deni. *Encyclopedia of Herbs*. Dorling Kindersley, 1995, 1996.

Chase, Pamela Louise and Johathan Pawlik. *Trees for Healing*. Newcastle Publishing Co. Inc., 1991.

Cunningham, Scott. *Cunningham's Encyclopedia of Magical Herbs*. Llewellyn Publications, 1985, 1994.

Densmore, Frances. *How Indians Use Wild Plants*. Dover Publications, 1974.

Erichsen-Brown, Charlotte. *Medicinal and Other Uses of North American Plants*. Dover Publications, Inc., 1979.

Foster, Steven. *Echinacea – Nature's Immune Enhancer*. Healing Arts Press, 1991.

Gilmore, Melvin R. *Uses of Plants by the Indians of the Missouri River Region*. University of Nebraska Press, 1977, 1991.

Hamel, Paul B. and Mary U. Chiltoskey, *Cherokee Plants*, 1975.

Hoffmann, David. *Holistic Herbal*. Barnes and Noble Books, 1996.

Hutchens, Alma R. *Indian Herbalogy of North America*. Shambhala Publications, 1973, 1991.

Kindscher, Kelly. *Medicinal Wild Plants of the Prairie*. University Press of Kansas, 1992.

Moerman, Daniele. *Geraniums for the Iroquois*. Reference Publications Inc.

Moore, Michael. *Medicinal Plants of the Mountain West*. Museum of New Mexico Press, 1979.

Platt, Rutherford. *A Pocket Guide to Trees*. Pocket Books, 1952, 1972.

Reader's Digest. *Magic and Medicine of Plant*. Readers Digest, 1994.

Stark, Raymond. *A Guide to Indian Herbs.* Hancock House Publishers Ltd, 1981, 1992.

Stuart, Malcolm. *Herbs and Herbalism.* Van Nostrand Reinhold Company, 1979.

Sweet, Muriel. *Common Edible and Useful Plants of the West.* Naturegraph Publishers, 1976.

Thistle-Dyer, T.F. *The Folklore of Plants.* Singing Tree Press.

Tierra, Michael. *The Way of Herbs.* Pocket Books, 1980, 1990.

Vogel, Virgil J. *American Indian Medicine.* University of Oklahoma Press, 1970.

Weslager, C.A. Magic, *Medicines of the Indians.* Signet.

Westrich, LoLo. *California Herbal Remedies.* Gulf Publishing Company, 1989.

Ywahoo, Dhyani. *Voices of our Ancestors.* Shambhala Publications, 1986.

index